DON'T FORGET TO DANCE

Don't Forget to Dance

A Unique Alzheimer's Journey— from Bizarre to Blissful

A memoir

by

MARC ALDERDICE

Adelaide Books
New York / Lisbon
2021

DON'T FORGET TO DANCE
A memoir
By Marc Alderdice, PhD

Published by Adelaide Books, New York / Lisbon
adelaidebooks.org
Editor-in-Chief
Stevan V. Nikolic

For any information, please address Adelaide Books
at info@adelaidebooks.org
or write to:
Adelaide Books
244 Fifth Ave. Suite D27
New York, NY, 10001

ISBN: 978-1-956635-78-2
Printed in the United States of America

Don't Forget to Dance is dedicated to Mary, my wife of forty-five years, who is still the love of my life eleven years after being diagnosed with Alzheimer's. How she prepared herself for many years in advance of her diagnosis to help ensure her later happiness in the event she would develop Alzheimer's like some of her family members—and how her approach to life after the diagnosis worked to enable her, and me, to enjoy the best life possible no matter what—are truly amazing. I appreciate her now more than ever. She would be honored and thrilled for others to learn from her problems and solutions.

Contents

Acknowledgments

My sincere gratitude to Michele Chynoweth, a superb editor and book coach as well as best-selling author, without whom this book would never have been completed in an acceptable manner for a reader to enjoy. I had written many scientific journal articles, protocols, and other "just the facts ma'am" reports. Believe me, writing a memoir is totally different, and this was a true learning experience for me. Like all editors, Michele loved the phrase "show not tell" that drove me up a wall. But she didn't just tell me to do this, she showed me how to do it and she was phenomenally patient…but always driving towards the final goal.

I want to express my appreciation to Herta Feely, an editor and writing coach at Chrysalis Editorial, who reviewed and provided helpful comment on my first draft, as well as those who read drafts at different stages and provided objective input and advice to make it a more readable story.

I also thank our sons, Jeff and David, and David's wife Arlyn for helping to fill in a few scenes or gaps in order to ensure everything presented is accurate and true.

Finally, I want to thank and honor all the caregivers who have cared for Mary with all the love they've shown so that Mary has felt she's truly loved by all in her time of need.

Introduction

This book was written for several reasons. It started with me putting my thoughts together to process what was happening and assess how to better take care of Mary, my wife of thirty-four years at the time, who was diagnosed with early-onset Alzheimer's disease at the young age of fifty-nine. Her journey and mine have, of course, been intimately intertwined, as they always are for those with Alzheimer's and their families.

It's difficult to know the best action to take or words to say when you're with a loved one or friend who has such a condition, especially as unexpected events or conversations arise, which happens often. I needed some way to help me know what to do, and how to react, on a consistent basis instead of merely acting on my own thoughts, feelings, or frustrations at any given moment. Writing these thoughts to better address Mary's needs, tracking what was tried and what did or did not work, has consequently helped me better adjust to my own needs. These experiences have provided me with new insights and appreciations for those with Alzheimer's or who are impaired in other ways.

Mary's journey is similar to those of others with Alzheimer's in many respects, but I also realized over time that everyone's path is different. Mary experienced a variety of bizarre behaviors that I could have never imagined in my wildest dreams.

As she started having problems, I made notes of what transpired to help me remember details so I could better convey them to various professionals for her treatment. I subsequently developed this book as a labor of love for Mary, because she is a shining example of how to prepare for dealing with such a devastating disease, as well as how to approach life in general. What she did long before the diagnosis of Alzheimer's is remarkable, and how she handled herself afterwards is phenomenal. I think everyone can learn something from Mary regarding how to prepare for their own futures, whether they think they might develop Alzheimer's or another debilitating illness, or they just want to move through the normal aging process in a happier frame of mind.

Another reason for writing the book, and what motivated me to carry it through to completion, was my desire to share what I've learned—much by trial and error—with others facing similar experiences. I've certainly made my share of mistakes dealing with Mary in different situations, but I learned from them and hope to help others avoid my pitfalls.

I realize each person's journey is unique, but there are a lot of common issues we all must face when someone close to us is suffering with Alzheimer's. I believe this book can be a guide for coping with the present, planning for the future, and doing one's reasonable best to prevent guilt and regrets from rearing up over the past.

While a caregiver can never truly be prepared for everything that can occur, I believe the saying, "forewarned is forearmed" can be a big help. It's important to be prepared to deal with changes in behaviors and emotional needs ahead of time as much as possible, or at least be aware such anomalies can happen, so someone doesn't panic or go off the deep end when changes do occur. I know I wish I knew then what I know now.

Ideally, by sharing our journey, this book offers some hope it doesn't have to be all bad, that good times with your loved ones can occur, and you and they can be happy.

Many have asked me about the origin of the title, "*Don't Forget to Dance.*" Over time I have often wished I could have a "do-over" on numerous parts of my life. If only we could go back in time! Mary always loved to dance, but I didn't and was never good at it. In the old days, if we were at a social event where there was dancing, I always danced to a few token songs, usually slow ones with her—undoubtedly not as many as she would have liked. I've felt a lot of regret about missed moments such as these.

Mary has continually loved to dance throughout her journey, and fortunately we've done a lot of dancing, almost every day to some extent, over the past several years. It hasn't been the type of dancing like we used to do before her disease took hold, but both she and I have loved it. The dancing we've done during this period has served as my do-over, and both Mary and I have made the most of it.

Don't Forget to Dance reveals how Mary has lived life to the fullest, how she filled her heart and mind with good thoughts and positive actions for years *before* she was diagnosed, especially from the time she realized Alzheimer's might be in her future— and how she "danced" through life well *after* her diagnosis.

Chapter 1

Beginnings

I was driving fifty miles an hour down Maryland Route 108, taking Mary to her doctor's appointment. She was already upset about my "kidnapping" her and snapped, "You're going the wrong way."

Just desperately wanting to get there, I kept my eyes on the road. "We've gone there before. We'll be there in a few minutes." I tried hard not to overreact, knowing from experience where such interactions could lead.

"You need to turn around...*now!*" Her voice was louder, emphatic now, but also tinged with a hint of panic.

"This is the way to your doctor. We'll be there soon. Then you'll see," I stated a little more forcefully, trying to be reassuring.

She sat forward in her seat, glared at me, and started yelling. "You have to turn around because you don't know what you're doing. You are going the wrong way. Turn around!"

I replied as calmly as I could, "We are going the right way. We'll be there in just a few minutes. Everything will be okay as soon as we get there." My logical explanation made no impact, as was often the case at this stage. Trying to convince her otherwise was useless and only inflamed the matter, whatever the perceived issue was at the time.

Suddenly, she unbuckled her seatbelt, turned to face the passenger door, opened it, and attempted to leap out of the moving car. I stepped on the brake and simultaneously grabbed her seatbelt which was already retracting, clenching it tightly to keep her in the car with one hand, trying to control the steering wheel with the other. I could see the road through the open door and hear the whooshing of the pavement rushing by as I stopped her from jumping out just in time.

"Mary...stop...settle down...it'll be okay." I gulped for breath in between words, my heart still pounding from adrenaline and fear. Entwined with the sheer panic was a surreal numbness as if I was overlooking this whole scene and was not really a part of it. *Is this really happening?*

I held onto my wife tightly, gasping for breath and grasping for reality. I slowed the car until we settled back into our seats, and then gathered enough courage to approach the speed limit again. I never did fully stop the car, too afraid that Mary might try to jump out again and run off.

She remained fuming mad the rest of the ride but at least had calmed down physically to the point she was controllable enough for me to continue driving to our destination, all the time holding onto her seatbelt.

Once my heart started beating normally again, all sorts of thoughts raced through my mind. *Was there anything I could have done differently before reaching this point? Were all her years of preparation a waste?* And even more scary—*Is this only the beginning?*

Mary and I never would have met if it wasn't for buzzards! In 1975, I moved from Texas, where I had lived all my life, to

Connecticut for a postdoctoral fellowship in pharmacology. This was in January, so the winter weather was quite a shock. I often left work at night when the temperature was well below freezing, it was snowing, and a strong wind was making the wind chill factor sink to depths that froze my thin body to the bone. Many nights I had to muster all the willpower I could to open that exit door of my work building and slog down the long hill to where I had parked, shivering and miserable.

I left work one Saturday evening in mid-March with grand plans to shop for a guitar that night and teach myself how to play. As I entered my apartment complex, I noticed a flier on the bulletin board. It was an open party invitation to "Celebrate the Buzzards Returning to Hinkley, Ohio." It seemed logical this was a going away party for Mr. and Mrs. Buzzard, awkward name as it might be.

It was not in my nature to show up at a party where I knew no one, but uncharacteristically, I decided since I still hadn't met anyone in the area outside of work, I would gather the courage and go.

Hesitating and pacing in the hallway for an inordinate amount of time after finding the apartment in a different building, I finally knocked. A nice-looking young lady in her mid-twenties with short dark-brown hair opened the door. Without giving her a chance to utter a word, I asked, "Is this where the party is?" thinking as soon as the words came out, *Man, that was corny and stupid.* Although there was a wall at the end of the entryway and I couldn't see anyone else, the emanating sounds of music and people talking made that obvious.

She gave me a friendly smile. "Where are you from, anyway?" She asked this in a light-hearted, welcoming tone, not in a condescending manner.

Knowing my heavy Texas drawl was overbearing, even to my own ears at times, I replied, "Texas, but I live in one of the other apartment buildings."

"Well, welcome. Come on in. My name is Shirley."

She led me into the kitchen, offered me a drink, showed me where the snacks were and introduced me to a few people.

I knew my accent would sound funny to them, since it was so different from theirs, so I initially felt a little ill-at-ease, but everyone was so friendly that I soon got over my insecurity and started to feel a little more comfortable.

After making some small talk and eating a few munchies in the kitchen with a group gathered there, I gracefully excused myself from their ongoing conversation among friends and meandered into the living room. Looking around, I noticed two young ladies talking quietly. They too were attractive and about the same age as Shirley, both with medium-length brown hair. They sat on the floor by the sofa, lady-like with their legs folded under them and to the side. They were talking to each other but glanced in my direction when I entered the room.

Not wanting to go back into the kitchen and interrupt the more boisterous conversation there, and not wanting to make any more of a spectacle of myself than necessary, I quietly moseyed over, squatted down without sitting so as not to be too intrusive or presumptive, and introduced myself. They politely said their names were Mary and Natalie and told me they shared the apartment with Shirley.

After feeling comfortable enough, I finally sat down with them and joined their conversation. We talked for a long time about where we worked and where we were from, the usual small talk. I learned they both worked in local elementary schools, Natalie as a teacher and Mary as a speech therapist teaching speech-impaired children. While she later denied it, I think Mary initially considered me as a new speech therapy challenge.

"So who are the Buzzards?" I eventually asked innocently, which sent Natalie and Mary into a fit of laughter.

Mary finally caught her breath and stopped laughing when she noticed my discomfort.

"Shirley moved here from Ohio. Every year on March fifteenth, Hinkley celebrates the return of the buzzards, or turkey vultures, to their town. It's sort of like the swallows returning to Capistrano, but not as romantic of course. There's apparently a big celebration every year on the fifteenth. So, Shirley talked all of us into holding a party in honor of..."

"The return of the buzzards," I finished her sentence and laughed at myself.

Mary smiled at me warmly.

Before I knew it, the party was over, and I was the last guest to leave. As I was turning to head out, Shirley asked for my phone number on behalf of the three hostesses so we could all get together again.

I arrived home from work the next day having already given up on my guitar career, feeling good about meeting my new friends from the night before. The apartment didn't seem so lonely for a change. Just as I was cooking some Hamburger Helper, the phone rang. It was Mary, inviting me over for dinner with the gang. I happily accepted the invitation, stumbling over myself to quickly turn off the stove and throw the half-cooked remains of my lovely dinner into the fridge.

I found out later Mary had taken the paper with my phone number and hid it from the other girls so she could be the one to call and invite me.

We had a really good time that evening and I was feeling great about my three new "girlfriends." That is, until after dinner when the three of them took dishes into the kitchen. I could overhear some of their conversation, and one of them (I think it was Shirley) said, "He's really a squirrel, isn't he?" The other two girls readily agreed.

I was devastated. In Texas, at least where I grew up, being called a squirrel was not good, meaning a person was weird in a bad way. Since all of my interactions with them had seemed extremely positive, I let it slide that night, not saying anything.

But a nagging thought lingered in the back of my mind, so a couple weeks later I asked Mary about it. She assured me it was positive and felt quite distressed I had taken it as a negative, saying that in their locale, "Being a squirrel means someone is fun and nutty in a good way." *Go figure.*

Looking back now, given our different accents and the fact that some of our words or phrases had different meanings, I'm surprised anyone even talked with me! While it definitely wasn't a positive attribute overall, Mary said she liked my accent and didn't want me to lose it.

We all got together on a regular basis after that, mainly Mary, Natalie, Shirley, sometimes another guy or two from the party, and me. I'm not sure how much of it was influenced by the fact that Mary was the one to call me that first time, but she and I quickly gravitated towards each other, started dating, and soon became a "couple."

Accents aside, Mary and I also had quite different backgrounds. About the only way we were alike was the fact that both of us had always been studious, constantly striving to receive straight A's and be at the top of our classes.

Both of Mary's parents worked in factories. Her Italian mother was more strong-willed than her Ukrainian father, so she was the dominating influence in the family. Her father was a tinsmith and could make or fix anything; Mary was proud of him for that. They had always lived in Waterbury, Connecticut and in the same house since Mary was in elementary school.

I don't know a lot about Mary's growing up years as she never talked about her childhood much. She had a sister, Sue, who was ten years younger, and two brothers, Greg and Mark, in between. From the little she did tell me, I gathered that her parents were over-protective. She once said that because she had some visual problems and wore stronger prescription glasses, she was never taught how to ride a bicycle, plus being a little overweight may have added into the mix. She was also always quiet and reserved. All these factors together apparently led to her having limited social interactions growing up, except of course with all her immediate and extended family.

Whether by desire or necessity, she became even more studious in high school, although she did take judo and earned a brown belt. But quite often she would come home from school in a down spirit. Food was always important and plentiful in her family, so often her mother would say, "Here, have a brownie. It'll make you feel better." This mindset stuck with her and affected her weight and self-esteem for many years. Ironically, the only job Mary had before graduating from college was working in a bakery one summer while in high school.

She had a few friends outside of her family growing up but didn't go on a date until her senior prom. She was all excited someone even asked her. Little did she know at the time it was arranged by her mother and the mother of a boy who was planning to go into the priesthood. It was his first date also. But they had a great time and Mary didn't learn about the arrangement for a long time. Many years later I communicated with her date, now a priest, via email when Mary was invited to a class reunion. He told me about when he picked her up, saying, "I was waiting in the living room. When she came out, she stunned me because she was so beautiful."

It was only after she went off to college and lived in a dorm away from home, and then later shared the apartment with Shirley and Natalie, that she was able to flourish, making friends and not having restrictions.

She initially majored in Spanish and spent her junior year in Spain. When she came to the realization that she would never be able to speak or teach Spanish like someone raised bilingual, she switched her major to speech pathology, receiving a master's degree. Fencing seemed to be her primary out-of-her-shell activity, at least in graduate school.

My upbringing was a lot less sheltered. My family moved every one or two years until I was in high school where we stayed a whole three years. From the time I was born until my high school years my dad was a school principal in various small Texas towns, a job that didn't pay much back then. My mother was a music teacher which paid even less. We always had the necessities, but I'm sure I learned my lifelong frugalness from my mother. To provide for his family, my dad would go from job to job to advance and make a higher salary. Since he was highly respected, he was always offered the new position.

My brother, Joe, was four and a half years older than me. We got along well, but we were brothers after all. With the age split, he had his set of friends and I had my own. I'm not sure how many of my "friends" were actually friends because my dad was their principal, but I always seemed to make one special friend everywhere we lived.

I was always thin, and I remember Joe telling a friend of his, "Marc's so skinny, he has to run around in the shower to get wet." While that may have been somewhat of an exaggeration, I've never been the epitome of manly physique.

That said, in my two junior high years I played a lot of sports—football, basketball, and even participated in most track events. For these two years we lived in Gail, a west Texas town with a population of around one hundred. Buses brought in kids from all over the county, so if almost everyone didn't play sports, we would hardly have had enough for an eight-man football team. Admittedly, I was never good at these sports.

In Gail, there was only one boy, Ron, who was my age in the whole town, so we were destined to be best friends. We also brought out the daredevil in one another.

My father had a single-shot 22-caliber rifle that Ron and I would use to hunt rattlesnakes. We were hardly ever successful hitting a moving snake, but we learned two important lessons—how to reload quickly and how to run fast.

One time I crawled down a natural hole in the ground I could barely fit through—to see what was there of course as boys do. It was dark down there so Ron and I later returned with flashlights. I could see that the hole descended about five feet, opening to a small cavern starting about three feet high. Once down there, I saw it tapered down in all directions. I also saw that there were thousands, likely millions, of spiders scurrying in all directions. They were granddaddy longlegs, which I knew weren't harmful, so it didn't bother me while I was crawling around. I've since heard there are two such critters that look similar in those parts, one that had a venomous bite and one that didn't. I'm not sure which one, if not both, was down there but I'm definitely thankful I didn't tick off their whole galaxy.

Over the years I've learned there's often a fine line between adventurism and stupidity. While the frequency of my doing something most would consider ill-advised diminished as I grew older, my willingness to step out and take a chance, trying what was not necessarily the standard, has paid off in how I've been able to approach dealing with Mary's later problems with Alzheimer's.

I got my first job in Gail. Ron and I chopped weeds out of a cotton field for a few weeks. We also walked along the side of the four roadways leading out of town, picking up soft drink bottles people had tossed out of their windows. We cashed them in for a whole one or two cents each. My guess is we made about three cents for each hour of being out in the sweltering heat.

While in Gail, my father developed ulcers due to all of the stress of his job, so he started selling insurance and we moved to Odessa. Like I said, in Gail, the thing to do was play sports, so when I went in to register for high school in Odessa, I planned to sign up to play football. Thank God the registrar kindly advised me to head in another direction by telling me I might have too heavy a schedule to play football. It was Permian High School, the school featured in the movie *Friday Night Lights* starring Billy Bob Thornton. Football was serious business, it was rough, and the players were all two to three times my size (I was likely about a hundred pounds at the time) with twenty times the muscles.

It would have been a disaster in more ways than one, and I would not have lasted long for sure. To be honest, I never liked getting hurt and was never good at football anyway.

This was an early lesson for me not to continue doing something just because it was expected or always done a certain way, which also helped me later when dealing with Mary's Alzheimer's issues. Regretfully, it was a lesson I had to re-learn several times over the years.

I worked at several places through high school and college—from cafeterias to Six Flags Over Texas, then eventually in a hospital lab. My college housemate at the time worked in a hospital lab and liked it, so I applied at a different hospital. They had no openings and I had no such experience except from my chemistry lab courses, but I told the pathologist, "I'll make a deal with you. I'll work for you for nothing as long as the lab technicians teach me what to do as they have time. After that, you can start paying me once you feel I'm adding value." It was an offer he couldn't refuse.

I started by washing all the test tubes, flasks and beakers, and soon I had learned to run enough tests where I was worth getting paid. I worked there mostly nights and weekends for seven years while taking a full load of classes in the mornings with labs in the afternoon, all the way through graduate school. This was one of the times I was most well off financially. I always had spending money because I never had any time to spend it.

As it's been said, "necessity is the mother of invention." I guess you could say that growing up I learned to be resourceful and unafraid to try something different—traits that would once again prove to help me later in dealing with Mary's disease.

I was soon introduced to Mary's family, and we went to her parent's house usually once a week, especially for Sunday dinners and holidays. There was always a feast. The Italian side dominated the household, especially when it came to food and the large number of local relatives who loved to gather often and eat. The pasta, Italian sausage, meatballs with hard-boiled eggs in the middle and pasta sauce were fabulous. There were always special traditional foods for Christmas, New Year's Eve and Easter. Their living and dining rooms were combined into one big room, so on these occasions extra tables and folding chairs were arranged to accommodate everyone.

There was always an over-abundance, and over-indulgence, of food. I think Mary's mother actually tried to fatten me up, which I didn't mind in the least.

One evening, Mary and I were sitting on the floor of my apartment, talking about anything and everything and nothing. We eventually arrived at the topic of what we wanted for the future. As we were going through ideas, Mary said matter-of-factly, "I've always wanted a fireplace."

After pondering it a bit, I thought I would seize the moment, responding with, "I'll get you a fireplace someday."

She sat up straight, eyes wide open, and asked, "Are you asking me what I think you're asking me?"

All I could think was, *did I really just ask her what she thought I asked her?* We had been "hitting it off" for a while and I knew she was the one for me. We were happy together. While I had no intention of asking her to marry me that evening, it now seemed as good a time as any. *Besides,* I thought, *I'll avoid the awkwardness, and possibly expense, of a formal proposal.*

Still, I felt a little reticence with the suddenness of such a big step, and almost spoiled the romantic moment. "It depends on what you think I'm asking," I said coyly while thinking *you chicken.*

"Are you asking me to marry you?"

Here goes, I thought. "Yes."

She was shocked to say the least. "I was not expecting this, and it's taken me totally by surprise, but yes, yes, yes!" She giggled girlishly then gave me a big hug.

I must admit this was an extremely quick, and not very well thought out, proposition much less marriage proposal. But I didn't feel any regrets, and we both knew it was right.

If Mary seemed shocked, you should have seen her mother! For several generations in her family, it was expected that offspring would be born, raised, go to Catholic school, get married to a local person in the parish church, raise children, work, die, and be buried in Waterbury. Moving was frowned upon. Mary once told me that one of her cousins married and moved to the next town over, which was maybe twenty to thirty minutes away, and that her aunt felt like it was the other side of the world.

I soon learned there was another family tradition with which I would have to contend. In their family's culture, a couple typically just "hung out" together for a while, then dated for a year or two or even longer, and this courtship was followed by an engagement which lasted for a minimum of one year so the wedding could be planned appropriately. Plus, they were all Catholics, so getting married in the local Catholic parish church was a given.

When I came on the scene, I blew their traditions apart like an atomic bomb. I was both a foreigner and a Protestant who was moving way too fast. Mary and I met in March, became engaged in July, and married in December, all in the same year. So needless to say, it took a while for her family to get used to me—although they really didn't have too much time—and eventually accept me as part of their family.

While we were engaged, I took Mary to Texas to meet my mother, father, Joe and his wife Kay, and my few other relatives. Mary was very excited about it all, both to meet my parents, with whom she loved to talk over the phone, and to travel to Texas. Before this trip she had not been further west than Scranton, Pennsylvania or further south than New York City. She loved my parents, calling them Mama and Daddy in the Texas fashion, and they immediately and lovingly embraced her as their soon-to-be daughter-in-law.

Our wedding was right after Christmas and the ground was covered with several inches of fresh snow. We were married in a small white Protestant church with a tall steeple and a red door. It was the typical, picturesque, New England church I had always envisioned.

Mary wore her mother's altered wedding dress, which was full length and had a long train. Mary and Natalie had traveled to New York City to find a pair of special shoes for Mary to wear with her dress. On our wedding day, with the half-foot of snow, Mary didn't want to wear these new, and expensive I might add, shoes from the car to the church, so she wore some old hiking boots with several people holding up the dress. In all the busyness and excitement, no one thought about changing shoes. Halfway down the aisle she realized she was still wearing the boots, but no one could see them, and it made no difference to me—I just thought she looked beautiful.

We were married about mid-way through my two-year fellowship commitment in Connecticut and moved into an apartment located between where she and I worked.

Mary was serious in a number of ways but was usually looking for fun—to turn ordinary times into extraordinary ones. One evening in the dead of winter, when the temperature was below freezing and it was snowing heavily, we took a walk in a new neighborhood under development near our apartment. No one lived there yet, so we were walking in the middle of an unplowed street with six to eight inches of fresh snow unscathed by cars. New houses were in the process of being constructed, and we were wondering how anyone could ever afford them.

All of a sudden, Mary jumped forward, fell to her back on the ground, and started waving her arms and legs back and forth. I thought she was having a seizure!

"What on earth are you doing?" I asked. "Are you okay?"

She got up quickly without disturbing the surrounding snow and made a big jump towards me, sporting a proud smile. "Making a snow angel, silly."

Being from a place with scant, if any, snow, how was I supposed to know what a snow angel was? But there it was, perfectly shaped in all its glory.

Not too long after we married, I asked her, "How many kids to you want?"

She said, "Six. How many do you want?"

Gulp! I replied, "Two."

Mary became pregnant about nine months later. I was offered a position on the faculty at the Louisiana State University Medical Center to teach pharmacology and conduct basic research, and we moved to New Orleans when she was about five months into her pregnancy. I know a few "hit" contracts were probably put out on me by a couple of her Italian family members for breaking with tradition, especially taking the pregnant daughter of a possessive mother to a place where all sorts of unspeakable crimes are committed, or so it was thought by those who never left the Northeast.

That's when our life together really began.

Chapter 2

Family Life

Jeff was born about four months after we arrived in New Orleans. A few months later, I again asked Mary, "How many kids to you want?"

She replied, "Four. How many do you want?

I said, "Two."

David was born three years after Jeff. Not too long afterwards, I asked Mary yet again, "How many kids to you want?"

She quickly replied, "Two." I never bothered posing the question again, satisfied with the answer.

After living in an apartment for a year, we bought a house we could afford (with mortgage interest rates extremely high at that time) on the West Bank of the Mississippi River at the end of civilization on reclaimed swampland in a new neighborhood that flooded every few years. For a while, there was an alligator in the drainage canal that divided the neighborhood. What we didn't realize at the time was that some of the people who moved into the new neighborhood thought they were moving into the city.

Many of our neighbors were true Cajuns, great people once we got to know them. Bushel baskets of shrimp, crawfish or crabs, whatever was in season, were bought right off the boat not too far down the road. A neighbor boiled them in a large caldron with potatoes, corn, onions, and great Cajun spices. We would put a sheet of plywood over two sawhorses in a driveway, cover it with layers of newspaper, pile on whatever was cooked in the middle, and dig in and socialize for hours. It was a great time.

Mary was busy raising the boys, but she decided to use her speech therapy education and training by working part-time through an agency to rehabilitate stroke victims in their homes. This was admirable but didn't last too long. With all the travel time and costs, certifications, state licenses, continuing education, agency fees, insurance costs, and of course baby-sitter expenses, it was a losing endeavor.

We started going to a church on the East Bank where the main part of New Orleans is located. This church had morning and evening services on Sundays, so we sometimes stayed in the area and attended both services instead of making the long trek back and forth from where we lived. In between services we took in the various sights.

We often visited the French Quarter around Jackson Square, always going to Café Du Monde, famous for its powdered sugar-coated beignets; we all loved them, and this was a special treat. Mary and I always indulged in their chicory café au lait and the boys had chocolate milk. They were mostly covered in sugar by the time we left.

The café was right on the other side of the levee from the Mississippi river, so we sometimes strolled up to the top of the levee to watch the huge cargo ships, tankers and barges navigate around each other and the bend in the river. It was interesting, if not somewhat scary, that the water level and ships were above the level of the French Quarter. There were a couple of large, old-fashioned paddle boats from the Mark Twain era stories. These were fun to ride, especially when we showed visitors around.

Sometimes we just walked around the streets of the French Quarter, gawking at all the ornate wrought iron balconies, shops, and eclectic décor. From the streets we peeked into cloistered courtyards protected by high gates of intricate iron work. Sometimes we strolled down Bourbon Street, which thankfully had been cleaned from the wild night before, admiring the street corner artists and musicians.

We seized the opportunity to take jaunts to other area attractions too like the Audubon Zoo. The boys loved seeing the animals and going up Monkey Hill, constructed for kids to climb since the area was so flat. This seemed a safer option than the river and canal levees built all around New Orleans to keep it from flooding. We rode the trolley down St. Charles Avenue through the Garden District to see the large, old restored houses. We toured several plantations. Even the cemeteries were interesting since people were "buried" above ground to keep the caskets from floating up with the high water table.

Mardi Gras was the most interesting time of all. Dozens of parades flooded the streets with huge floats and costumed riders throwing thousands of strings of beads, candy and toys to the crowds. Undoubtedly, if you were a guy, the best way to get noticed and catch the prime stuff was to have a kid on your shoulders.

We lived in the area for six years. Once I knew we were moving, I went alone to Bourbon Street in the French Quarter on Mardi Gras day at the height of the festivities to bid farewell to this crazy city I had grown to appreciate. I would always remember it fondly as the place where Mary and I really began our lives together as a family, away from our relatives on both sides.

After New Orleans, I took a position with a pharmaceutical company in Evansville, Indiana to set up and conduct clinical research trials. My first trip there for an interview, as I was driving through town I thought, *why would anyone want to live here?* It was definitely not as exciting as New Orleans!

But it turned out to be an idealistic place to raise the boys.

Evansville is on the Ohio River, which made it interesting by itself, with its annual *Thunder on the Ohio* hydroplane boat races. There was a zoo and a children's museum the boys loved, and the schools were great. What made it extra special were the lakes which were just a couple of hours away in several directions.

I bought an old red boat and we started water-skiing. We often took a coworker of mine, Phil, with us so we always had two adults in the boat, one to drive and one to watch the skier. The less powerful a boat, the harder it is to get up on skis, and my old boat wasn't very powerful, so it took strength and stamina. Phil and I were able to get up out of the water rather quickly. Mary tried super hard the whole first summer but could never do it.

Late that season, Mary, Phil and I took the boat out one last time. Even though the water was cold, Mary knew it was her last chance of the year, so she wanted to try again…and she was determined. She kept trying to hoist herself up out of the water time and time again, refusing to get back in the boat. It became dark, bugs were out, and now even the air was cold. I pleaded with her each time, waving at her to come back into the boat and get warm and dry, but every time she failed, she repositioned herself and motioned us to take off again.

Finally, mercifully, she got up! We could see her proud smile from the boat and were cheering ecstatically. She didn't ski long, maybe fifteen seconds, because she had become so exhausted, and let go of the tow rope. We pulled the boat around, but she was too weak to climb the ladder, so with effort we helped pull her up. She sank into a back corner, curled up in a ball, and shivered. She was truly blue in color, and we covered her with all the towels we had. As miserable as she was, I think that was about the happiest I had ever seen her. She was so proud of herself she just kept giving us a huge smile as she shook from the cold. I think it took several days to pick all the bugs off her teeth she was smiling so broadly being pulled behind the boat—okay, that's a slight exaggeration. Mary never had a problem getting up on water-skis again.

Mary's determination to not give up and perseverance to get through difficult times were attributes that paid off numerous times in her life's journey to help ensure happiness.

Jeff and David always loved being pulled behind the boat on various tubes or other platforms to sit or stand on, plus they also became quite proficient on their smaller kid skies.

The boating became too much to do in one day though, travelling to and from home to the lakes, so we started camping. Mary loved to camp and would have likely gone every weekend if we could. It took a lot of time and effort to get everything ready, drive, set-up the tent and campsite, go on the lake several times, tear everything down, pack it up, drive home, and then unload and clean up. In my opinion, it was often not worth the effort to go for one night, but we did because Mary loved it.

We camped and skied at all of the lakes but our favorite spot to camp, boat, and enjoy nature was Piscah Bay on Land Between the Lakes in Kentucky. We had great times there as a family, and I can't think of another surrounding where Mary was happier. She truly blossomed with the outdoor activities. Once when we were there, enjoying it so much, I joked that when I died, I wanted my ashes scattered there. Years later Mary remembered what I said and was planning to do that for me—or maybe I should say *with* me.

One day, Mary was preparing chicken in the kitchen. Our younger son David, just four at the time, was watching closely and asked, "Mama, where does chicken come from?"

She told him, and a couple of days later he asked, "Where does steak come from?" She answered. It was the first time he realized chickens and cows had to be killed for us to eat the meat.

Nothing more was said at the time, but a few days later he informed us, "I don't want to eat meat anymore. I don't think animals should be killed for us to eat them."

David was a strict vegetarian from the time he was four-and-a-half years old to the time he was six, but he ate eggs, milk and cheese. We respected his desire, and Mary accommodated his diet in many inventive ways.

While traveling, we always stopped to eat at a restaurant with a salad bar for him. I vividly remember one time. There was a huge salad bar and lots of items. I went through it with David, asking him if he wanted each item. This took quite a while since he was too short to see most items, but we had developed a perfect masterpiece with exactly what he wanted on his plate. We reached the end, and I asked him. "Do you want bacon bits?"

"Are they real or artificial?" he asked with a resolute tone.

"Well, I'm not sure, let me ask the waitress."

As the waitress walked by, I asked her. She replied, "Oh, I'm sure they're artificial."

David nodded okay, bacon bits were added, and our long-awaited, triumphal perfection of a salad was complete. On our way back to the table, the waitress came to me and said, "You know, I wanted to make sure, so I asked the chef." She told me proudly, "The bacon bits are real bacon."

I looked down at David who heard this.

He looked up at me and simply shook his head slowly back and forth with a determined look.

I sighed, handed the plate to the waitress, and we started all over again. We developed another plate, but it just wasn't the same. This reminds me of when I've carefully crafted a lengthy email, written exactly the way I want to say it, and for some interstellar or mystical reason, or my fault, it gets deleted, and I am never happy with the wording the second time.

The above salad bar incident occurred on a road trip when we were going to detour through New Orleans on the way back to Evansville. We visited our old neighborhood and had a crab boil in the driveway, like old times. Jeff loved it, but David peeked cautiously over the edge of the large table at all the crabs piled up. He left to go run around some, soon returning. Mary and I noticed a little hand reaching over the top of the table picking up some crab meat Mary had started piling up.

David took it in his hand, examined it, and looked questioningly at Mary who looked at him caringly and said, "It's up to you."

He cautiously put it in his mouth, chewed a moment, reached for another piece, ate it and left. A few minutes later he was back, eating his share of crabs.

We didn't make a big deal about it. The next day as we were traveling, we did our usual salad bar stop at a brunch buffet where he succumbed to a significant amount of bacon and sausage. The pattern had been broken...but only for a time. David became a strict vegetarian through middle school and high school, never looking back, and has now been a vegan for many years.

Jeff liked the fact that his younger brother was a vegetarian. Every time we ordered pepperoni pizza as a family, David always picked off his pepperoni slices and put them on Jeff's pizza.

Growing up, David was somewhat more gregarious and always wanted to talk with almost anyone, including strangers in public places, which was always embarrassing to Jeff. Once we were walking into a store with a "No Soliciting" sign on the door.

David asked, "What does that say?

Jeff was quick to tell him, "It says 'No Socializing.' It means you're not allowed to talk to anyone in the store."

Our Evansville times were also great ones and we would have continued to live there, but after six years the company division I worked for was planning to relocate to New York City, or at least so I thought at the time. Not NYC types, we started looking for a new place to live, work and play.

I took a similar research job with an Italian pharmaceutical company starting a US subsidiary. It was known at the time the company would eventually locate somewhere in the Washington, DC area, but the temporary offices were in Newport Beach, California. I spent three months in a Residence Inn there while the kids finished the school year.

Once they were out of school, a moving company packed up and stored our possessions, and we all spent the summer in southern California. What a great time! We saw all the sights and had The Beach Boys blaring as we drove around. The boys even went to a Boy Scout aquatic camp. We were told the small shark usually swimming in the little bay never bothered anyone.

At the end of the summer we moved to Gaithersburg, Maryland.

Unlike Evansville, there wasn't a convenient place to water-ski as most bodies of water, at least within reasonable distance, banned gas-powered boats. So, we took up a different water sport—whitewater rafting.

I don't recall which it was, but one river had a spot called the Devil's Elbow, a ninety-degree turn in a narrow bend with a significant drop and rapids. Mary and I were riding in the back of a six-man rubber raft when her side bounced hard up against a large bolder just as we were making the turn, sending her flying into the air, landing back down on me and forcing us both overboard. We were caught in the undercurrent for what seemed like an eternity. Knowing this was a dangerous spot, the rafting company had staff on the side of the river throwing us ropes and yelling to grab one.

In retrospect, I find it amazing how I couldn't fathom what all was going on around me in such a rapidly changing situation, focused on my sole intention of trying to keep my head above water. All turned out well, and we were jumping off a cliff into the river about ten minutes later.

Little was I to know at the time that we would later navigate the raging waters of Alzheimer's with more than a few Devil's Elbows.

During the years we lived in Evansville and Gaithersburg, my jobs required a lot of travel, both in the US and internationally, up through when Jeff and David graduated from high school.

I was able to take Mary with me on a few trips, as well as our sons individually. David was into music and went with me to New Orleans. I had to attend meetings a couple of days, but we went to the Jazz Fest, which was a big open-air event, and two nights we went to Preservation Hall in the French Quarter until it closed in the wee hours. Jeff went with me to South Africa, where my meeting was at a game reserve, with us being the ones locked in a compound as opposed to the animals.

Our sons always played well together, whether with GI Joes or gearing up in different hero costumes, but later followed their separate paths.

Jeff loved Cub Scouts, Boy Scouts and Civil Air Patrol, where he became the Cadet Commander of his squadron. Later, he trained as a firefighter and EMT starting in high school, then joined the Marine Corps shortly thereafter (he shipped out for Boot Camp at Parris Island, South Carolina five days after his high school graduation). He later got a bachelor's degree in Homeland Security, then a master's in Disaster Medicine and Management. He now works in emergency management and teaches lots of related courses. He always made sure his shirt placket, belt, and zipper fly were all in perfect alignment.

David was more free-spirited and would never keep his Cub Scout shirt tucked in his pants. The regimented life was not for him. He was more artsy and went the musical route, starting with playing violin using the Suzuki method but fairly quickly changing to drums. Since guitars were much easier to carry around than a drum set, practices were usually in our basement—loud, but there was no doubt where he was. He's since taken up all sorts of percussion, including hand drums and marimbas. He's a great teacher and organizes a lot of school and community events.

Our sons' differences had their advantages. Since neither would be caught dead doing what the other enjoyed, there was little competition between the brothers. David religiously followed his vegetarian, now vegan, path, and Jeff didn't think it was a meal unless there was a dead animal on the plate.

And although our sons turned out to be very different from each other, they both had one thing in common: they did what many people likely don't do or don't get to do—they followed their passions.

After both sons graduated from high school, we moved from Maryland to Virginia, close to Charlottesville, where we lived on four acres in a rural area. Mary absolutely loved where we lived, as did I. This setting seemed to be idyllic for her. We had big windows overlooking a large side yard where deer often grazed. During winter when the trees were bare, we could see a mountain range. We also took up kayaking. Mary loved floating through the water seeing cranes, egrets, even beavers at times.

We lived in Virginia when the 9/11 attacks occurred and the Iraq war started. Jeff's Marine Corps Reserves unit was called to active duty and within a short time he was shipped to Kuwait for staging. He was the commander of a Light Armored Vehicle (LAV) and was in one of the initial groups sent across the border into Iraq doing reconnaissance and other combat operations before, during and after the invasion.

Rick Leventhal, with Fox News, was embedded with the battalion Jeff was in, and he aired live reports on television when he could, so we generally kept the TV on in case there was a special report. I distinctly recall one morning Rick was reporting live, riding in an LAV somewhere in Iraq. He couldn't provide the location or specifics and we didn't know if he was with Jeff's company or not. Suddenly, he was interrupted by loud automatic gunfire. He said something like, "Oh my gosh, we're under attack." Then the transmission stopped. No one with the network knew what happened and they couldn't reconnect with Rick. It was about two hours before he came back on the line to report that the unit had been ambushed but all Marines were safe, and they were on their way again.

These were the longest two hours of my life, and I think I aged a few years. I was a wreck with worry. Mary handled it much better than I did. She told me, "There's nothing I can do for Jeff in Iraq except pray for him and his safety. I've turned over keeping him safe to God and accept Jeff will be okay."

Mary's prayers worked for her and, as it turned out, Jeff was not part of that group.

Still we continued to worry and pray as Jeff continued his patrolling, sometimes weeks at a time in a four-LAV platoon, sleeping in holes they dug in the sand, or often just sitting in the seats in their vehicles. He did a total of three tours in Iraq, after which he got out with an honorable discharge and numerous service-connected disabilities. It was a rough time for all of us, but especially Jeff.

David was with us some, but he mostly stayed in Maryland living with friends. He spent his time primarily playing gigs with different groups and recording in a studio. While we were living in Virginia, he went to Colorado to visit a friend who had recently moved there to check it out. David has lived there ever since.

One day I received a call from people I had worked with at a previous firm offering me a position, still conducting clinical research trials, with a new business they were starting in Rockville, Maryland to help pharmaceutical companies develop new drugs. I had loved working with them so I took the new offer with one stipulation: I could work from our home in Virginia most of the time and just go into the office every two or three weeks for a few days. This way we could continue to live in Virginia. They agreed, and I accepted.

A year later, they offered me a promotion with one stipulation: I needed to be in the office full time and would need to move back to Maryland. Mary and I discussed it with a lot of careful consideration and consternation, and I decided to take the job. Mary was sad about moving but okay with it. In the end, it seemed like the right decision—it was time to pull up roots and leave friends behind once again.

Mary found the move this time to be more difficult than she had in the past. She understood and didn't complain, but she was initially feeling down about it. We moved to Olney, Maryland which was at least close enough to reservoirs where we could continue to kayak.

Several years after we moved my father passed away, and the following year Mary and I took my mother to Colorado to visit David. There was a special concert being recorded by PBS in Beaver Creek featuring Feast, a Celtic classical group David helped form.

Beaver Creek was about a three-hour drive from where David lived. After the concert, once all of his equipment was packed up, we drove over a high mountain pass late that night to get back to his house. About midnight, we stopped at the top of the peak. A million stars shone magnificently in the crystal-clear night sky, taking our breath away like nothing we had ever seen before, even on our many camping trips. I glanced over at Mary and her look of total awe made me believe she felt like she was in heaven that night in Colorado.

Our travels and moves to different places were fun and adventurous in a lot of ways, and everywhere we lived was interesting. But while we discovered we could develop friendships anywhere, the trouble with moving a lot was that friends were left behind, and as good as our intentions often were, it wasn't easy to maintain contact for very long. Life had a way of getting busy and moving on.

We discovered that a variety of frequent moves makes it difficult to form and keep long-lasting, true friendships. For example, Mary's apartment mate and good friend Natalie got married, but although we went to the wedding, we haven't had contact with her and her husband for many years.

Jeff and David met new friends wherever we moved, but it was especially difficult for them to say good-bye to those being left behind. I think the moves made it even more important to ensure our families remained close, so we traveled a lot to see them or arranged for them to come visit us.

My Dad's mindset regarding moving for jobs was evidently ingrained in me—always to make an improvement in one way or another for my career and thus presumably for our family for the long term—or so it seemed at the time. Looking back and knowing what I know now about how important it is to have long-lasting, close friendships when your family is suffering with the disease of Alzheimer's—those that can only be developed through experiences with the same people over many years—I'm not so sure I would have made the same choices.

But then again, it's easy to look back and second guess yourself.

As we moved around and became a bit older, Mary and I sometimes talked about where we might like to retire as many couples do, dreaming about our future together later in life. There was no one special place we ever settled upon, and we usually ended up agreeing it would depend on where our sons (and future grandkids) were living. In retrospect, it's probably better we didn't try to make more definite plans.

Chapter 3

Mary's Renaissance

During our marriage, Mary endured cycles of losing weight and subsequently gaining it back, each time gaining a few more pounds, becoming a bit heavier than the time before. This was especially evident both times she was pregnant. With her genetic tendencies to be overweight, plus her upbringing of overeating, it was understandable to me why she might eat more than she should and not feel bad about it. Food essentially uplifted her spirits. But she increasingly started to struggle to control her eating. It got to the point that when she saw a photo of herself from the back she said, "I cannot believe that's me!"

Not too long after this epiphany, a talk with Heather, one of her friends, made a tremendous impact. Heather was an alcoholic but was in recovery and hadn't had a drink for many years. She and Mary were together often when we lived in Maryland.

One day they went for an outing together. While driving back home, Heather told Mary, "I want to stop by a bar on the way home, play some pool, and have a few beers."

Mary was shocked and fervently tried to talk her out of it but couldn't. Heather was insistent. After lengthy attempts at rationalization, Mary finally told her emphatically, but lovingly, "Please take me home first. I can't bear to watch this happen to you or be a part of it, knowing how devastating it was for you in the past."

Heather turned to look at Mary and said, "Aha, now you know how I feel every time I watch you eat too much and take extra helpings when I know you're not still hungry. I've been watching you gain more and more weight. You're ruining your health. To me, since I care so much for you, watching you put more food in your mouth is like you watching me take a drink."

This was a life-changing moment for Mary. After numerous failed attempts, she knew she couldn't change her bad eating habits on her own, so she joined Overeaters Anonymous. Essentially, Mary learned sugar was to her body the same addictive "drug" that alcohol was to her friend's. Shortly thereafter, she joined a more rigorous arm of OA called HOW, which stands for Honesty, Open-mindedness, and Willingness. In this program a sponsor held her accountable for what she was going to eat on a meal-by-meal and snack-by-snack basis, planned out in detail the day before. Soon Mary was sponsoring others in the program.

Within a little over a year, Mary was down from her top weight of a little over two hundred pounds to the lower one-twenties, where she stayed for over ten years until Alzheimer's started getting in the way. Mary was enormously proud of this accomplishment and would be delighted for me to share this if it could help others with similar issues. She looked and felt better, and she was totally uplifted with a renewed spirit for living life to the fullest.

Some of her most fun times were shopping in the petite section at a clothing store. She had never been able to do this at any stage of her life before she practiced her program. I can still vividly see her bouncing between the racks of clothing like a teenager, holding clothes up against her in front of a mirror and smiling proudly—not in an arrogant manner, but delighted in herself that she had accomplished something so life-changing.

She always had nice medium brown hair, usually keeping it draped over her shoulders a little. After losing the weight she ventured into other looks to enhance her new appearance and outlook. Sometimes she colored it with a reddish flair, sometimes with blonde highlights, and quite often she wore it in a ponytail to match her new girlish feeling and figure. This new persona and look allowed her to virtually relive her younger years and make up for lost time, and it helped her become more independent and outgoing.

The weight loss was one of the best things that ever happened to her. It improved her happiness and our overall marriage in several ways. Yes, I'll admit the rigor of her food plan could be aggravating at times, especially when traveling or eating with others who weren't familiar with the program. But she was so much happier with her body in general and was able to do a lot of physical activities she loved that she could never do, or even try to do before.

She ate right for the next twelve years. Her diet included lots of berries and other foods known to be good for the brain, and possibly even slow the onset of Alzheimer's.

Mary's father was diagnosed with Alzheimer's in the mid-1990s and died due to complications from a fall in 1998. Her mother passed away in the year 2000 from medical problems but also seemed to start showing signs of memory issues toward the end. But it was one of her dearly loved aunts on her mother's side of the family who was diagnosed with Alzheimer's and passed away from the disease in the mid-1990s that made the biggest impact on Mary.

Mary had told me over the years about her aunt being so sweet and how she would do anything for her niece and her family. My wife told me of many fond memories she had spending the night at her aunt's house when she was growing up. I also came to know her well through various family gatherings. Mary's aunt would never hurt a flea—okay, for full disclosure, especially in her retirement years, she did enjoy watching wrestling every Saturday night. Sadly, as Alzheimer's took its toll, she became belligerent and actually started physically attacking others with her cane.

Mary heard and saw first-hand, through her father's disease but primarily by witnessing her aunt's drastic character transformation, how people could radically change when their Alzheimer's progressed. She knew people often said words or exhibited actions and reactions that were not normal for them. She saw how people with the disease could often lose control, blurting out whatever was in their minds or thought processes at the time, which could be very unkind and even hurtful to others.

With such a diagnosis being present on both sides of her immediate family, the thought of possibly developing such a disease was especially horrifying to Mary. However, she realized there was a chance, likely a greater chance than the general population, she might eventually suffer the same fate.

She and I had also heard a story about my grandmother dying of some type of dementia when I was quite young. We had been told by other family members that even as she was bedridden, my grandmother was telling her caregivers about God as best as she could and praising Him, and reportedly brought one of them to accept Him. Mary once mentioned she hoped that if she ever did develop Alzheimer's, she would be like my grandmother.

Mary had a servant's heart and always wanted to help people. She knew individuals personally or became involved with support groups for people who had problems with weight, physical health, and mental or emotional issues. She was always available for these people and did whatever it took to help them through their tough crises or stay on track in between.

Years later, after Mary's diagnosis, Jeff told me he remembered a time, likely when he was in early high school, when his mother just started crying with him and David there. Mary told them she was thinking about her father who had started having problems with dementia. She made a request, "I want you to promise me that if I ever get sick like your grandpa is, that you will remember me how I am now and not like I'll probably be after I get sick."

One evening while sitting in our living room, I noticed Mary pacing some on the other side of the room, looking deep in thought, touching her index finger to her lips like she often did when she was serious. She came over, sat on the sofa next to me, looked me in my eyes, and made sure she had my attention. "Marc, since some of my relatives developed Alzheimer's disease, there's a higher chance I might also, and I realize it. I've seen the negative actions, as well as unkind and hurtful words that can come out of peoples' mouths when they no longer have conscious control over what they say. I don't want that to be me. I want whatever comes from me to be kind and gentle, and even a blessing to others if possible. I'm making a decision to fill my heart and mind and spirit with only good thoughts, so these will be the underlying feelings and emotions to come out if such a time ever occurs."

I was not expecting this conversation at all and didn't know what to say. I was stunned. This was obviously not a spur of the moment thought on her part. It seemed apparent she had been thinking about this a lot. By her downcast look, downhearted tone in her voice and somber demeanor at the time, it was obvious to me this had been weighing heavily on her heart for some time. Yet there was an underlying hopefulness in her at the same time. It seemed she at least had a plan to do what she could to make the best of it, one way or another.

She hadn't asked me a question, but I knew she needed a response and reassurance. I stood up, grasped her hands to pull her up, and we hugged for several minutes without saying anything. She was crying softly, and I felt tears fill my eyes.

Once I was able to talk without choking up while continuing to hug her, I said, "I'm very sorry you have to even think about such a potential future, but this is a great idea. I'm proud of you for wanting to approach this head-on. I'll help any way I can, so let me know what I can do. Whatever happens, we're in this together, and I'll always be here for you and with you."

This conversation occurred about eight years before she was diagnosed or started having any symptoms. We never talked about it again, at least in that context. But Mary committed to following through on her plan.

From that time forward, my wife became determined to prepare for the possibility she may develop Alzheimer's and to diminish the effects, delay the onset, and ready her heart ahead of time. She actively and purposefully pursued a multi-pronged approach in her life—encompassing mental, spiritual and physical components—during this "preparation" stage.

She made a conscious effort and intentionally prepared herself emotionally by filling her mind and heart with love and good thoughts. It was her nature anyway, but she always tried to have a grateful attitude so that saying "please," "thank you," and other pleasantries were natural responses. She tried to have a cheerful disposition and did what she could to help others.

Mary felt that her mind would naturally reflect what was in her heart if she ever came to the point that she wouldn't be able to "think" clearly anymore. She felt if such a time came—whether she expressed herself with words or in actions when relating to others—it would be her overall feelings of inner harmony that would take over—that not only would having this peaceful feeling in her heart cause her to have better interactions with others, but it could lead to her own contentment and inner happiness, even in times of adversity.

She watched no violent movies. She liked the Hallmark type of films, whereas I liked action flicks. Certainly, the *Rambo* movies with Sylvester Stallone were out. We did find some we could watch together that were action movies but most either featured elements of comedy, romance, or a departure from real life. Examples were *True Lies* with Arnold Schwarzenegger and Jamie Lee Curtis, *Undercover Blues* with Dennis Quaid and Kathleen Turner, and the Jackie Chan movies. Plus, she always enjoyed the TV show *Monk* with Tony Shalhoub.

Similarly, she equipped herself spiritually with a lot of prayer and Bible study. She loved God and wanted to grow closer to Him. She had strived for this since we married, but in retrospect it seems she worked harder at it during her preparation years.

Mary also pursued numerous physical activities during these pre-symptom years. She took long walks, went hiking and kayaking, did lots of yard work, and started ballet classes and ice-skating lessons. She tried to keep in good physical shape so she could continue to do the activities she loved. I'm sure most of the physical activities were the result of her being more active and energetic due to her weight loss, but I know there was at least a subconscious attempt to ward off Alzheimer's.

Somewhat related to how Mary planned for potentially getting Alzheimer's, she prepared to have substantial hearing loss. She had been wearing hearing aids for several years, and her hearing seemed to be getting worse. She started learning sign language so she would be prepared to communicate if her hearing was lost. She always liked to flash me the "I love you" sign made with one hand. She especially loved signing the worship songs at church as she was singing. I often watched her in admiration, and she was so caught up in the moment she never noticed.

Her food plan required a daily reading from the OA program book. After the reading, she wrote a page or two each day on what she thought about the passage and how she could apply it to her life. She never missed one of these assignments, partly because she was a strict rule follower, but also because she had to read her writing to her sponsor the next morning when they talked.

I was involved with her OA program to some extent from the time she started it. Occasionally she wanted me to read one of her writings, but this was her personal space and I purposefully stayed on the outside unless she sought my input. I knew she would be able to write her true feelings better if she knew I wasn't going to see it unless she wanted me to.

Her OA/HOW program involved me both directly and indirectly, as it took a significant amount of her time to do all of the calls, writings and food planning. Anytime we went out to eat she needed to plan ahead of time, either by taking her own food with her or knowing how much protein, starch, veggies, dairy, et cetera she needed at what time and, importantly, what substitutions were allowed.

Eating at a restaurant was often challenging since she weighed everything to make sure she had the right amount of each food item. I recall once she ordered four sides of vegetables one at a time so she could weigh each one to know how much more she needed to meet her required allocation. The waitress really looked skeptical and actually annoyed with these requests, likely wondering if Mary was checking portions for some restaurant association or health agency. I had to suppress a laugh when I saw her talking to her manager, looking in our direction.

There were sometimes difficulties going to someone's house to eat or to a gathering like a pot-luck dinner. It was often just easier for her to take what she needed instead of asking what the ingredients were in each food item, or worse, turning everything down. Unless the host was in the same food program, it was apparent Mary's bringing her own food was like an insult and seemed offensive or even embarrassing to that person when others saw what Mary was doing.

I recall a couple of times when the host asked Mary, "Is there something wrong with the food?" There were also a few times when the host's "look" portrayed it all—as if to say, "How dare you judge my food like some health inspector scrutinizing how it was prepared or the size of the portions?" To make matters worse, when it came to vegetables or salad, Mary's required portion could take much of the whole amount prepared for the group. After a few such occasions Mary learned to take what she could gracefully and supplement it with more once we were home.

Still, the years during this "preparation" period were great ones for Mary. Mentally, she was doing lots of studying and writing in her journal, all of which she enjoyed. Physically, she was at a healthy weight, keeping busy with activities she loved to do such as walking, dancing and kayaking, and even starting new ones like ice skating.

Spiritually, her reading, studying, writing, and praying brought her closer to God. I could tell by the way she so thoughtfully and diligently prepared for a Bible study, or how she smiled with joy every Sunday in church while singing the worship songs.

She was inwardly and outwardly happy. She felt good about herself. I could tell by the exuberance she radiated when she talked about or planned activities. There was a certain spark about her—like she had found her true self, the person she always wanted to be. I'm so glad these years were such happy ones for her. This was her personal renaissance.

We rarely if ever talked about Alzheimer's or the possibility during these years. I knew that the subject had to be lingering in the back of her mind, but she didn't outwardly obsess over it or let it run her life or ruin ours at the time. In general, Mary prepared for her future well-being, whether that future was to include Alzheimer's, hearing loss or just growing older.

I was proud of Mary for all she did leading up to her Alzheimer's diagnosis, but I became especially impressed by how she approached life and what she did after receiving it. What I couldn't even imagine at the time was the horrendous turbulence ahead and how her preparation years would allow her to be in a truly happy state despite it all.

Chapter 4

Devastating Diagnosis

Alzheimer's is an insidious disease, and I have learned there's no "moment" when, all of a sudden, a person knows they have it, as would be the case with a stroke, heart attack, or another health problem. Mary's early symptoms were gradual, and I believe typical for what is common for most Alzheimer's patients. It's difficult to remember exactly what became evident, or at least to what degree, before versus after Mary's actual diagnosis, but her symptoms were much more subtle before compared to after. She and I both noticed the onset in various ways.

In retrospect, I believe the first indication, which at the time I didn't really consider a problem related to early dementia, occurred when we were driving to Texas for my father's funeral. Halfway there, I asked, "What did you bring to wear to the funeral?"

"What I'm wearing." Mary matter-of-factly pointed to the stretched out, casual, black sweatpants she had on.

This took me by surprise for sure. I felt my jaw drop and sighed. I was speechless for the moment, wondering if she was joking. We were too far into the road trip to turn back at this point. After a few long moments, I realized she wasn't kidding. "You're going to need something a bit dressier, so we'll stop at a mall once we get there," I suggested.

This incident in poor judgment or inability to think through a situation logically or thoroughly occurred close to a year before her diagnosis, before her forgetfulness became obvious, at least outwardly. It seemed to be an isolated occurrence with a period of normalcy for months afterward. Subsequently, changes were subtle but gradually increased. There was nothing significant, but small missteps started happening more frequently.

Mary initially exhibited the normally expected issues for early Alzheimer's. For example, there were the typical lost or misplaced articles. Sometimes she was looking indecisively for something, but didn't know what it was, or at least couldn't explain it. She also started asking the same question several times over a short period. She more frequently forgot why she went into a certain room. If I noticed she was just standing and looking around, I often asked, "Are you looking for something?"

She often replied while still scanning the room, "I came in here to look for (or to do) something, but now I can't remember what."

Mary's vocabulary was always broader than mine, but she started being unable to think of the word she wanted to use, which naturally frustrated her. Sometimes I could fill in the word for her without making a big deal out of it. Other times, without hesitation, she used a similar word in the same general category as the word she would normally use (like pen for pencil or clock for watch), but this didn't seem to bother her because she didn't realize it. I tried to never question any misstatements she made so as not to upset her.

Both Mary and I noticed increasing problems with her memory lapses, but I imagine Mary realized the start of them before I did, since all I could do was observe what she did or said. I'm sure she sensed confusion internally before I noticed anything outwardly. However, over time I was more mindful of her forgetfulness than she was because I remembered the things or issues she had forgotten.

There were times I didn't notice anything different, when she sometimes told me, "There's something wrong," or "Something's not right." But after a while, when the episodes became more routine, all I had to do was see the anguished expression on her face to know what she was experiencing.

In the beginning, we were both in some stage of disbelief or denial this could be happening to us. I was probably in denial more than she was. The more I realized what was transpiring, the more worried I became about Mary and how our future would be affected. While the possibility of Alzheimer's had been in the back of her mind for years, I was just realizing the enormous reality of what it might mean, and it was scary.

Regardless, she wanted to confront the problem and not put it off, especially in the event something—anything—could help. We had considered the need for her to get evaluated but became side-tracked and always put it aside because her problems were initially so mild and infrequent. It was sometimes easier for both of us to minimize her forgetfulness or attribute it to getting older than to confront the looming "elephant in the room."

Jeff and David often knew something wasn't quite right when they were around, and we would look at each other, perplexed and worried. We ignored or often tried to cover for her mistakes when possible. This could be in the form of helping her find a word, finish a thought, put something in context, or make sure everything was provided or put out in the right sequence for preparing a meal.

Mary and I finally started talking about getting a professional evaluation, broaching the subject gently, speaking to each other in general terms. I could tell by the frequent forlorn expression on her face that she was seriously concerned and scared about what was happening to her, likely knowing deep down what the diagnosis, and thus prognosis, would be.

Still, part of me wanted to stay in denial or at least ignorance. Besides the smaller episodes—when she lost her keys, wallet, book, or didn't always prepare what was needed for meals—I conceded to myself that there weren't any "big" incidents that had set off any "flares." *After all, similar symptoms can be the result of other "fixable" conditions*, I calmly reminded myself. *Maybe her issues were due to thyroid problems, impeded blood flow to the brain, vitamin deficiencies, or whatever.*

It was Mary who made the definitive decision to be evaluated by a specialist. I had gotten to the point of strongly recommending this to her, so I was thankful when she finally said she wanted to see someone. I had heard of situations where family members thought a loved one needed to be evaluated, but the affected person refused to accept the possibility and wanted his or her life to proceed as usual, leading to difficult family situations. I was fortunate my wife made the decision herself.

She was standing, pacing a bit, while I was sitting in my recliner paying bills one evening. I was busy but felt an eerie presence. I turned to see Mary inching closer, hovering above me. I looked up at her right at the time she said. "Marc, I want to be evaluated by an Alzheimer's professional." Her voice sounded apprehensive and somewhat defeated, yet also had an optimistic overtone.

I got up and hugged her, relief flooding through me. "I know this is difficult, but I think that's a great idea. Let's get you checked out thoroughly and see what's going on."

"I want to have this done as quickly as possible." Her tone was adamant.

"I'll start checking for the best place right away. And remember, we're in this together." I held back tears of pride that she had made the difficult decision that I was afraid to initiate and couldn't make for her.

We continued to hug for a while, holding each other tightly.

My background is in pharmaceutical research, and my occupation for many years has been to set up and manage clinical research trials to study new drugs for different diseases. I've even performed a couple of studies on Alzheimer's. Mary knew how these studies worked from me and wanted to participate in one if possible.

I looked on the Internet and made some calls to clinics in the region I thought might be conducting such studies to see if any were recruiting patients at the time. We discussed it and decided to have her evaluated at the Memory Disorders Program at Georgetown University Medical Center where such studies were routinely conducted. They had a couple of Alzheimer's studies with experimental treatments that were either ongoing or about to start where new patients were being enrolled. We took their earliest appointment available.

Mary was eager to do this but, as expected, quite apprehensive, both about the testing and the potential verdict. No one wants to take a test if they know they're going to "fail" so she was anxious. She displayed an uncanny combination of eagerness and nervousness, almost like when we were about to hit some potentially dangerous rapids during one of our rafting trips. She wanted to do it…but didn't want to do it. She wanted to know…but didn't want to know. Nevertheless, we both knew that a thorough examination at an experienced clinic was the best way to know for sure and receive some treatment that might help.

We went for our initial assessment, which was about an hour drive through Washington, DC traffic. Mary was quiet the whole way there. I did most of the talking, making some positive statements about what we were doing, plus trying to make some small talk as a distraction to the thoughts likely bouncing around within her.

Once we parked, it seemed like it took an eternity to reach the clinic, almost as if the next step was surreal or in slow motion. While we checked in, Mary was friendly and cooperative, but then she was nervously subdued while interacting with the clinic personnel.

Mary answered many of the intake questions, but I needed to address a number of them that she couldn't. In some cases, I believe she was afraid she might say or do the wrong thing, knowing everything would be judged and likely recorded by the staff and filed away in their records. It seemed for her almost like going into a job interview, dissertation defense, life-saving surgery, or jury trial—all with a pass/fail result.

She received a thorough assessment with lots of tests, including blood and urine tests, a neurological exam, brain MRI, cardiovascular assessment, and sonogram to check carotid artery blood flow to the brain. Many of these tests were to help rule out other potential causes of confusion and memory loss. She underwent a battery of standard memory tests, which were to assess her level of cognitive impairment. I was allowed to be in the room with her the whole time and could tell she was nervous. Before leaving that first visit, we briefly discussed with the head nurse our desire to be in a clinical trial. We left feeling something was accomplished and, more importantly, something good might come out of it for her.

On the way home, we looked for places to eat during future trips. With Mary's food plan she couldn't eat just anywhere, plus it needed to be planned in advance. There was a McDonald's where she could work in two side salads and one packet of the dressing she liked, so we planned to stop there on the way home from future visits.

We scheduled another visit with an outside Alzheimer's testing group in Virginia to conduct a more comprehensive exam for memory and overall cognitive ability. I couldn't go with her into the testing rooms like I was allowed to at the memory clinic. Altogether the visit lasted two to three hours, which seemed like forever.

I was anguishing in the waiting room, pacing, continually looking at my watch. I knew what Mary must be going through—that she was feeling frustrated and incompetent. Those types of tests for that length of time would be confusing and stressful for anyone, but especially for someone with her difficulties. I did see her during a couple of short breaks. She was stressed and almost in tears. As she came out the last time, I could tell she was beaten down, didn't want to talk, wanted to sink into a hole, and there was nothing I could do or say to lift her out. She was exhausted and we didn't talk much on the way home. We both went to bed early that night and just cuddled until falling asleep.

A week or so later, after all the tests were completed and the results evaluated, we were called back to the Georgetown clinic. We were a whole lot less eager about this visit. Instead, we felt a foreboding sense of dread. The trip to the clinic was long, somber, with little talk. All I could do was anticipate what they were going to tell us. Interestingly, I also felt a strange sense of optimism and hope, or at least a glimmer of sanguinity, since I knew we were advancing one step closer to finding out something, whatever that might be, and possibly being able to do something about it. Mary seemed to have a similar feeling but was more subdued.

We entered the clinic, signed in, were greeted by one of the nurses, and were asked to wait in one of the examination rooms where Mary had been tested previously. I sensed that she was uncomfortable going back into one of these small rooms with a plain table and chairs where the examiner sat across from her asking lots of questions (sort of like they do on those TV cop shows when you're arrested). She was solemn and silent. Nothing I could think of to say seemed appropriate, except for small talk that sounded like obvious small talk. So I was quiet too after a few minutes and I mostly held her hand and rubbed her cheek and neck when the silent waiting became too awkward for anything else.

We were finally called into the doctor's office. I felt a sense of doom walking in, and Mary's face confirmed she felt the same. It was like walking into the principal's office knowing you're guilty. But this was worse, much worse, because we knew it would affect our whole future, not like receiving a lecture or temporary suspension.

The head memory care doctor was sitting, and we were asked to sit, with two of the nurse specialists standing close to us. The doctor briefly stated all the results were back.

My wife had Alzheimer's disease.

Mary had nothing to say nor could she really talk at the time. She seemed in a daze, as if she were disconnected from the conversation. Her silence spoke much louder than words. The doctor went on to tell her that she would be prescribed an approved drug for Alzheimer's. He mentioned there were some new drugs being developed and that they were participating in clinical trials to study them. He added that Mary could be evaluated to see if she qualified for one of these studies if we wanted. That was his basic message, which seemed matter-of-fact, even callous. We were dismissed to go with the nurses, who were also the study coordinators for the clinical trials, to take the next steps and deal with the emotions of the message.

After leaving the doctor's office, we talked with the head nurse in more detail about available clinical trials. Mary didn't say much except when asked a question.

"Does that sound okay to you?" the head nurse asked.

Mary nodded and said, "Okay," but looked lost.

I asked for and took home an informed consent form to review the details of what would be involved with the study. Having written informed consent forms for such studies before, I knew how scary they could sound since all potential problems have to be stated.

We both felt we knew what the diagnosis was going to be, but the verdict was still devastating, especially because of the unemotional way it was conveyed to us by the doctor.

Maybe they're trained to be that way—to just deliver the facts. I don't recall the doctor ever showing any real empathy. *I guess it's an everyday occurrence for them, one more diagnosis of many to add to the statistics,* I rationalized. *They're here to help but it's not their problem.* Still…it felt like a life sentence to us at the time.

After that meeting, Mary told me emphatically, "I don't like the doctor and don't want to see him again. I only want to deal with the nurses."

Fortunately, the way everything proceeded, we were able to honor her request.

The nurses were better than the doctor about talking through issues and being more nurturing, but of course they could only do so much. The rest would be up to us, the family members.

I recalled the Alzheimer's clinical studies I oversaw, evaluating responses from patients I never met who were profoundly distressed and often incompetent yet still realized their seemingly hopeless circumstances. It was saddening, but there was nothing I could personally do about it, except to make sure the study was worth conducting and provided reliable results. Now it was my turn to be on the other side, and I felt helpless.

Mary was prescribed Aricept, a medication approved for treating Alzheimer's, and she was told to start it immediately. However, in order to qualify for the clinical study, she needed to be stabilized on the medication for at least a month. This would allow her to take an approved drug to hopefully diminish the symptoms, in addition to giving her a chance to receive something in the future that might actually affect the underlying disease process.

The diagnosis itself didn't change the disease or the symptoms, but it had an enormous emotional and psychological impact. There was nothing different after that visit except the realization our worst fears were no longer purely some possibility that we rarely talked about. A real diagnosis of early-onset Alzheimer's disease at the age of fifty-nine was thrown on us like a huge, crushing boulder. All of a sudden, it was a reality, something tangible to be reckoned with.

We had a longer and sadder drive home from the clinic this time. Little was said, and Mary cried much of the way.

We didn't tell most people about it right away, but those close to her knew something was happening and weren't surprised. Once we did tell people, it was an uncomfortable conversation on both sides. While I regret it now, I informed our sons in more of a matter-of-fact manner since they knew she was having problems.

Jeff had returned to Maryland after leaving the Marine Corps about six months before his mom was diagnosed and started in the clinical trial. Over this time he soon noticed something was not quite right. I told Jeff while he and I were playing pool one evening. "It seems Mom may have the same thing her dad had," I said. Jeff knew she was getting assessed and was not surprised. I didn't have any real details at the time, so he mostly listened and nodded sympathetically, stating he was sorry this was happening.

When I told David over the phone, I don't think he knew what to believe. At the time, he had little trust in the established medical industry. He was more of a natural remedy person. His leeriness was at least partially due to a pain he once had in his wrist. Two doctors stated the problem was due to two different reasons and each was ready to perform a different type of surgery to fix it. David never did get the surgery and the pain went away.

David was well aware of the fact that his mother had never coped very well independently. For example, Mary was never good driving in unfamiliar areas or to unknown places on her own. She also had certain eccentricities just like anyone. She had always been wary of skulls and skeletons…a fear that seemed to be more heightened lately.

So David was in more of a denial than Jeff that his mom was given a name for her problems as defined by the medical industry. He felt her current challenges might be more of a natural worsening of issues she had always had, or possibly was due to something more natural like menopause.

But while our sons didn't see her as often, everything seemed to be more noticeable to Mary and me now. Problems with losing items, not remembering, forgetting words, all seemed to happen more frequently, or at least we were more consciously aware of them, after the diagnosis.

Still, at least we felt able to talk about everything more openly, which was good.

The required time on Aricept passed, and the next appointment was made. Mary seemed to have already declined some during this brief period.

I knew how much being in a study meant to her, so I kind of prepped her with answers since I thought she might score too low on the tests to be accepted into the study. I couldn't help with real memory items, such as her remembering words she was told during the testing. However, I mentioned the name of where we were going a couple of times in the car, pointed out which floor button I was pushing in the elevator, and mentioned what day it was in context with the appointment— all orientation items I knew might be asked. Since I had taken the lead for everything from scheduling the appointment to getting her to the right room, Mary would never have even thought about what floor we were going to. Every day was pretty much the same to her, so she would likely have no idea of these details if I didn't tell her at some time. So I didn't feel like it was cheating necessarily.

After she completed the main cognitive assessment test used for study entrance criteria, I noticed two or three nurses discussing Mary's chart in the hall outside our room, occasionally looking in and glancing our way.

Then the main nurse entered the room and told us Mary had scored one point too high to meet the entrance criteria. We both felt crushed. *This was all my fault. I shouldn't have prepared her at all,* I realized. While the results were encouraging in one respect, it would delay her participation in the study.

We returned a few weeks later for another screening evaluation. This time Mary didn't benefit from my "wisdom" in prepping—and she met the criteria, we signed the papers, and her participation in the study began.

Being in a research study provided some hope for Mary, although she realized the treatment was experimental, and it might or might not help. She understood it was a placebo-controlled study and she might not receive the experimental treatment. She knew the chances of the study helping her personally were slim, but she took comfort in the fact that the knowledge to be gained from the study, whether the experimental treatment worked or not, would help narrow down the focus for what might help others suffering from this devastating disease in the future.

At the time of her diagnosis, there were a couple of approved medications available that might help ease or slow the symptoms a bit, but none that would do much, if anything, to mitigate the overall long-term progression of the disease. The study offered a potentially better treatment.

The clinical trial required a variety of special procedures, including periodic MRIs of the brain, lumbar punctures, and lengthy intravenous infusions, so it wasn't a pleasant or low-commitment experience. But Mary accepted what she needed to do.

The loud noise of the MRI scanner was stressful and upset her the most. She was sensitive to loud noises to begin with, but it was scarier for her to be confined in a small area with the loud noise since the onset of Alzheimer's. She apparently couldn't fully comprehend everything was going to be okay while in the machine. Something that helped a lot was to have custom earplugs made that exactly fit her ears to muffle much of the noise. David used these for his musical events to prevent damage to his hearing, so we had an audiologist make a set for Mary.

It was distressful for me to see Mary's decline as she took the standard cognitive tests each visit. A vivid realization for me was watching how she drew the face of a clock less accurately over time.

I can't say Mary "enjoyed" being in the clinical study, but she looked forward to the visits and liked the study nurses. There was always the hope this new experimental treatment might help. Plus, we always had our special stop at McDonald's.

Hope didn't last long though. Mary was originally told she would participate in the study for two years and possibly longer, but her involvement only lasted about four months. The sponsor of the clinical trial discontinued Mary from the study because of some questionable finding on her MRI.

Needless to say, this news was again devastating to both of us, and it was another long and sad drive home. After this study termination visit, she didn't want to stop at McDonald's on the way.

Life would have been much less stressful if she hadn't participated in the study, but the hope of an effective treatment, if not a miracle, outweighed the inconvenience. At least now we had some confidence doctors were getting a little bit closer to finding a better treatment or even a cure.

But we had less optimism for our personal situation.

The clinical trial was a placebo-controlled study, so it's possible Mary was receiving nothing from the study medication that would help, even if the experimental drug did work. Knowing this didn't make any difference. She wanted to try something, anything, that could offer hope in an essentially hopeless situation, whether for herself or someone else. Fortunately, we didn't find out until much later that the whole study was eventually stopped because the experimental treatment was shown not to be effective. It's good we didn't know this at the time.

Reality sank in after she was taken out of the study, but we both accepted it as best we could, especially knowing there was nothing else we could do that we weren't already doing. There was no other acceptable clinical study available for which she qualified. Once we knew we had done, and were continuing to do, everything we could to treat the problem, it actually became easier to accept our situation and make the most of our time together. We didn't give up or give in, and we didn't let it totally consume us. We eventually realized we had to make the best of it, and Mary definitely made the most of it for as long as possible.

Chapter 5

Making the Most of It

After the initial bombshell of the diagnosis was followed by the lost hope from the clinical trial, there was a reluctant acceptance by both of us with the realization Mary's fate was now fact. However, she didn't want to merely sit back, give up, and let the disease run its normal course. She was determined to fight it, or at least make the most of her life despite it. She wanted to be active and do everything she could do or ever wanted to do while she was still able. You could say she came up with a "bucket list."

Her disease slowly progressed over the next two years. Early during this time, Mary came up to me all excited and said, "I want a dog, another Sheltie."

We had two Shelties, or Shetland sheepdogs, years ago, getting both as puppies. They both lived a long life. We had the first one, Missy, when we lived in New Orleans and then Evansville and the boys were young. The second one, Amber, we got shortly after we moved to Maryland the first time. We took them both to training classes and they were both well behaved and great companions, especially for Mary while I was at work.

But we were at another stage of life now. *I don't know if I can handle this on top of everything else*, I thought. *How will she possibly be able to train a new puppy, and how long will she be able to really take care of it?* But I couldn't say these thoughts out loud so instead I told her, patiently, like I would tell a child, "Mary, having a dog is a big commitment that will take a lot of time."

"I know, but I really want one. I think it'll be good for me to have it around the house during the day to keep me company, and we can go on walks together while you're at work." She looked at me with a new sparkle in her wide-open eyes, a huge bright grin lighting up her face. She had the same excited look as she did when making the snow angel, filled with glee. With the diagnosis and clinical trial still weighing heavily, I hadn't seen this exuberance in a long time.

I took a deep breath in and slowly exhaled. "You realize that it will take a lot of time for training? And that we'll need to take it to classes?"

"Yes, I know. But I really want one and it'll be good for me. Please…"

I just couldn't see this working out. Mary's Alzheimer's had started to take hold and I knew she couldn't be responsible for taking care of a dog, at least not the proper way or not for very long. On workdays I was often away from home for nine to ten hours, and picturing Mary alone all day caring for a rambunctious puppy was not a pretty sight…but then visualizing her home alone most of the day looked worse.

Of course, I didn't bring up her having Alzheimer's as a reason not to do this. She was so enthusiastic, even animated like a child while talking about it, and there were few things she had shown such excitement for the past few months since the diagnosis. Most definitely, I couldn't bring myself to tell her she likely wouldn't be able to do the training and upkeep for long. I knew our getting a dog was going to be a mistake, but I couldn't tell her no.

I sighed, then forced a smile and replied with outward enthusiasm instead of the inner dread I was feeling. "Okay, we'll look and see what we can find."

Her smile became a laugh and she threw her arms around my neck with a hug, shouting, "Oh, thank you, thank you!"

Our search for a Sheltie puppy began. We looked in the newspaper and on the Internet, searched at pet stores and visited veterinary clinics, and asked neighbors and people we knew at her food program group and my work. This effort was quite time consuming, but Mary remained excited.

Our two previous Shelties were females, and Mary heard males were more affectionate for this breed, so she wanted a male this time. She had heard how important it is to meet the mothers, since offspring often turn out to be like them, so this was important to her. We took several outings to check some leads.

We eventually discovered there were several Sheltie puppies for sale at four locations in "Amish country" Pennsylvania, all at least two hours away from home. So we took off one Saturday to check them out.

The first stop was an Amish farm. As we drove down the road to the farmhouse, there was a field between the main road and the house and barn complex. Manure was being spread from a large horse-drawn wagon. Close to where the manure was spewing, there was an adult Sheltie running around, obviously happy running through the manure, like a dog runs through a water sprinkler without a care in the world. Mary wanted a playful puppy, so this was looking hopeful. The owner showed us the one male puppy that remained. He was cute and a definite consideration, but we had more places to assess.

The sun had set and it was a little after eight at night, but there was still one more place to visit, a private home. I called the owner's cell phone to ask if it was too late. The man answered and said they wouldn't be at their house for maybe another hour.

Mary heard this and was noticeably disappointed. Since we were so far from home and might not be back any time soon, I told the man we would wait in the area and asked him to call me once they arrived home. He said to go on to the house to see the dogs, that the mother and last remaining puppy were in the detached, unlocked garage. It was good to know there were still people in the world who trusted other human beings.

We slowly opened the side door to the garage so neither dog could escape. Once inside, we turned on the light but initially didn't see either dog. Momentarily, the mother appeared from behind the car parked inside and walked slowly towards us. Mary knelt down to greet and pet her. The mother gently put her head down on Mary's lap in a loving manner, and my wife melted, happily crying.

"Oh, Marc, look at her. I've never seen a dog be so loving to a stranger. I want to take her home too. Maybe we can take both mother and son?" I knew at that moment it was all over without ever seeing the puppy.

A moment later, this puppy that had been recently weaned appeared from behind the car tire, running as fast as his short legs could carry him, in a bouncing romp, almost falling over himself, directly to Mary. Mary giggled and took him in her arms and cuddled him, all the time continuing to pet the mother.

The owners arrived, payment was made, and off we went. (We knew better than to ask about taking the mother dog, once Mary saw that she was quite attached to her owners.) All the way home, Mary cradled the puppy at her chest, kissing him, stroking him, cooing, and basically treating him like he was a newborn on the way home after she gave birth. I hadn't seen her this happy and excited for a very long time. She decided to name him Cody.

Cody was a good companion for her, at least initially, especially while I was at work. She, and I when possible, took walks around the neighborhood with him. We went to some training classes, but she was unable to follow through with the consistency she had with the previous dogs. In hindsight, an older, mellower dog would have been better than a puppy in need of intensive and consistent training. As an aside, I learned over time that being able to predict the temperament of offspring based on the mother is a total myth.

Mary loved to take long drives, especially during this time. A country girl at heart, she loved to go see fields, trees, ponds, horses, and whatever else might be out there. She especially loved the winding roads, the ones with "squiggles" (on the road signs) as she would say. On Saturdays and Sundays, we often took drives that lasted for hours, mostly commenting on the scenes with little substantive conversation, just soaking it all in. She would often say in amazement, "It's so beautiful." There were times I could see a longing in her eyes and expression as she looked out the window, like she felt she had missed out on her dream of being a true country girl. There wasn't much I could do about her desire except take her for these drives, so the jaunts were bittersweet.

But life goes on. Mary still loved being on the water, so we continued kayaking as much as possible. She was still strong and physically fit, and I found it was actually hard to keep up with her as we each maneuvered our kayaks along the reservoir inlets not too far from our home in Olney.

Sometimes I had to race to keep up with her and when I did catch up, she was always broadly smiling, filled with joy at just doing something physical and being out in nature. She almost exhausted me with the kayaking, and to this day I cannot understand why the wind seemed to change direction every time so that it was always briskly hitting me head-on to slow me down!

Filled with a new zest for life again, she started exploring new crafts and activities such as ceramics, pottery, and crochet lessons. The crocheting was challenging and didn't last long, but she did make (with lots of help) some of her own pottery and was proud of her achievements.

Mary always loved listening to our son David play the drums. Once while he was visiting, she decided she wanted to learn to play them too. She told me she was even having visions of playing in the church band in the future.

David started giving her lessons, writing down some simple rhythms for her to practice, and later listened to her play and tried to teach her over the phone when he was in Colorado. When they improvised she had so much fun, but when he tried to describe how the time was subdivided into notes and rhythms, she became lost quickly, not being able to comprehend what half of four was or two-plus-two beats were. This inability to do simple math prevented her from learning more. I worked with her and tried to help her as best as I could. This continued for several months, and she happily banged on the drum set in the basement until it became too frustrating for her.

Her willingness to try and learn new activities despite her difficulties never ceased to amaze me. As mentioned, growing up, Mary was over-protected, to the point of not being allowed to do some normal childhood physical activities, such as riding a bicycle. Thus, she never developed a good sense of balance. This always bothered her, and she wanted to make up for lost time.

We took Cody for walks in wooded parks, where he bounded over brush and branches. This was too enticing for Mary. She needed help at first, but eventually she followed Cody, walking on the fallen trees…without falling off! Soon she nearly skipped with enthusiasm, arms flung out and toes pointed, like a gymnast on a balance beam or ballerina, performing proudly like the young girl within her that she never got to be…until now.

I was proud she had the determination and fortitude to accomplish such feats at this stage. These walks were totally invigorating for her and seemed to provide her with a new appreciation of herself, likely hard to come by for most at this stage.

Mary had also always loved horses. She had ridden horses a few times before, mostly on the structured slow-paced trail rides. The one exception was when David arranged for us to visit a friend's ranch during a trip to Colorado about a year before Mary was diagnosed. She was able to ride a horse in a corral with no real restrictions. I vividly remember her excited, and somewhat scared, wide-eyed look and open-mouth smile when the horse broke into a gallop. She was exhilarated.

She now wanted to take horse-riding lessons. I called a few stables, and we rode out one day to check out a close one. As we watched an ongoing class for a while, it was obvious to me she wouldn't be able to keep up with a class of young students, so I arranged for her to start private lessons. I talked ahead of time with her instructor Kathy, telling her of Mary's condition and explaining that she would have to have extraordinary patience.

Kathy was a seasoned instructor who couldn't have been a better fit for Mary's needs. She took her time, starting with simple exercises; it took Mary several lessons to do what others could accomplish in one but Kathy didn't seem to mind. She didn't let Mary do anything unsafe, allowing her to only perform basic rudimentary maneuvers, and she had to back off some steps and start over at times. Mary's progression in this endeavor was nominal, but it didn't matter and she loved it. She was on a horse and actually taking lessons! This was one of the ways she truly "danced" in life, and I knew she was in heaven.

Watching her enjoy herself so much at this stage was a total delight for me, but it was also tinged with guilt. I wish I had realized her desires earlier, or had acted on them sooner, so she could have started such activities earlier in life when she would have received more out of them. We all have things in our past we feel guilty about, or at least wish we had done differently, and this is a regret of mine. Mary had always loved horses and I wish we had started her lessons sooner.

Mary could still drive to familiar places not far from our house and soon started going to a nearby senior center organized by the county. The thought of going to such a place could be a real downer for a lot of people, especially at her young age and with her diagnosis. But this was her idea and she wanted to do it.

She loved the physical activities and all the various arts and crafts. She especially liked doing ceramics. She often came home all excited about what she had made, showing each item to me with pride. We displayed vases, paperweights, and figurines she made or painted, decorating the house and my office at work. There was a lunch program available at the senior center, but because of her special food plan I made her lunch to take, which she greatly appreciated. Going to the senior center gave her something to do for much of the day while I was at work, which was good for both of us.

One day I surprised her with an unexpected visit to the center. It was lunch time, and there were several groups of people sitting together and playing games, eating and talking—except

Mary. She was sitting by herself eating the lunch I had made for her. My heart hurt seeing her so alone, but I mustered up a smile and sat down with her, trying to cheer her up with small talk.

Later that night Mary confessed that she felt like she had reached the point where she didn't fit in well. She told me she felt left out socially and didn't feel a part of the center any longer. It wasn't fun anymore and she wanted to quit going. I guess she finally realized that she was by far the youngest person there, yet sometimes felt older than the rest with her Alzheimer's since the activities and interactions were geared for people going through the normal aging process.

What to do next? I didn't want her to be alone during the day any more than necessary, as this wouldn't be good for her for several reasons.

Jeff lived locally and had a somewhat flexible work schedule, finishing a degree online while volunteering for the local VA hospital, so he was able to be with her some, but certainly not on a regular basis.

I arranged it so I could start working from home on some days. When I needed to go into work, I often came home to make Mary lunch and spend some time with her. I occasionally took her into work with me on Fridays when many people worked from home and few were in the office. She read, crocheted, or worked on her food program. She was just happy to be with me.

But there were other days, even though she had Cody and could initially still drive to close-by places, that Mary didn't know what to do with herself, ideally wanting me there all the time. She cried at times saying she missed me when I had to go into the office. She asked when I could retire and told me she would like that.

While I contemplated how it would have been nice to retire at the time and live a more carefree lifestyle with Mary, I wasn't sixty-two yet which meant I wouldn't even qualify for a reduced Social Security check…and I knew our financial future was more unpredictable now than ever faced with the uncertainty of Mary's healthcare costs down the line. Even if I wanted to stop working, much less retire, I couldn't. We had a large house payment, I didn't have a pension, and Mary was still young, now sixty, and physically healthy. The uncertainty of what type of care Mary might need in the future and for how long loomed large.

Plus, I wasn't ready psychologically. I enjoyed my job of managing clinical research studies to test new drugs for different diseases. My work made me feel I had a purpose.

While I wasn't ready to leave the workforce just yet, I started to develop a resentment—not of Mary but our financial situation. Now it looked like I might never retire. But I stuffed it down, resolving that both of us would have to make a sacrifice—planning for our future had to take precedence over what might be a temporary fix for what Mary and I felt we wanted at the time.

I saw only two real possibilities—hiring a caregiver from an agency to come and stay with my wife during the day or having her go to a private adult day care center.

As a first step I started asking Mary, "How about we have someone come to the house to stay with you during the day while I'm at work? The two of you could go shopping, take Cody for walks, or do fun activities together." Any time I brought this subject up I always painted it in a positive light and was careful not to use the term "caregiver."

She had never liked the idea of someone strange coming into the house and gave me an emphatic, "No" each time.

After a few failed attempts at exploring hiring a caregiver, it seemed the best option would be for Mary to go to an adult day care center. Following the senior center encounter, I was hesitant, actually a bit afraid, to bring this up to her because I thought it might signify a definite downward step.

I called and visited adult day care centers in my "spare" time, and left work early one weekday afternoon to check out an adult day care facility close to our house called Winterbrook. From the outside it was a sprawling, wood and brick one-story building, offset from the road by a small lawn and some trees. Once inside, it was very spacious with several homey, large rooms for people to watch TV, play games, do crafts, socialize, engage in singing and dancing, or have lunch. There was also a patio where some participants did some gardening.

There seemed to be something for everyone, and the people I saw seemed to be happy and having a good time. It was an active atmosphere with lots of attendees participating in a variety of organized activities, from painting to pottery.

I had a feeling Mary would like it there. But in all my wisdom, I took her by Winterbrook to check it out on the way home from church one Sunday, since we happened to be "passing right by." This was a real lesson learned as the timing could not have been worse. The center wasn't open to outsiders on Sunday, so there were no activities, but we were allowed in to take a look.

The only people there, except for a couple of staff members, were the handful of residents who were staying there in respite care at the time. They had finished lunch and most were sleeping. The place was "dead" and seemed more like the stereotypical nursing home. We walked around a little, and I showed her where I had seen the activities normally taking place, but to her at this stage, it was all an abstract and foreign concept that she couldn't envision even if she tried. Needless to say, she didn't like it and didn't want to go back.

A couple of weeks later I did convince her to check it out again. However, this time I made sure we visited on a "normal" weekday when we would encounter the regular group of attendees participating in the various activities. With advanced notice, I ensured the director and activities coordinator both knew we were coming and had availability to show us around. This pre-planning worked great and she agreed to give it a try.

Chapter 6

Social Scene

Mary had never been a social butterfly and usually didn't search out new people with whom to talk unless it was part of meeting and greeting new people at church or her OA/HOW program. She usually preferred talking one-on-one with friends and others who were part of a small group.

But all of her social skills gradually deteriorated with her Alzheimer's. After Mary's diagnosis, her contact with others was largely dependent on how well she knew someone. Successful interactions now required the other person's knowledge of how to communicate with her.

She no longer took any real initiative to talk to others— whether neighbors, church members or HOW meeting friends— seemingly because she didn't know what to say or how to relate, or maybe because she didn't want to put herself in an awkward or embarrassing situation. Since I knew her so well, I could tell how uncomfortable, sad or even "out of it" she felt, and this was very distressing to watch.

I was often around when Mary was on the phone with someone, usually from HOW. While face-to-face interactions were often problematic, I was amazed how Mary carried on a seemingly normal conversation over the phone. In most cases I don't think the person on the other end would know there was anything wrong. Likewise, if someone at church who didn't know her well started talking to her over the phone, they might not notice any problems.

But in person, if someone didn't know her condition, they sometimes thought Mary was unfriendly or even rude. I could tell by their looks or the way they cut the conversation short, which never helped.

People expect a two-way conversation, which Mary was often unable to engage in if she was asked a question and didn't know the answer, or worse, if she was expected to continue a dialogue by coming up with her own topics to talk about. She might remain silent, which was always taken negatively if someone didn't know—and, more importantly, understand—her condition. Regretfully, even the people who knew Mary had Alzheimer's didn't know what to expect or how to talk to her.

Overall, it was best for me to be with her when she interacted with others who weren't close friends. I could answer for her or rephrase a question so she understood it, or simply keep the conversation rolling by filling in the gaps. But of course, I couldn't be there much of the time.

On occasion, a couple of ladies asked Mary to join them on walks around the neighborhood, which was appreciated by both of us. However, Mary would tell me afterward that she was unable to keep up with their conversation and couldn't add much. Sometimes, she said, the others would continue talking for periods of time without involving her, and she felt left out and self-conscious. But I really couldn't blame the other ladies. I came to the realization that Mary being with others for the sake of being with them was not a good situation if the interactions emphasized her inabilities, or she didn't feel a part of the group.

Fortunately Mary's food program had always included a lot of social contact. She and her sponsor exchanged calls daily, and she had "hook-ups" or phone calls with other program members every day. Outside of me, this program had been Mary's primary social connection.

The HOW program had been great for Mary. It certainly worked from a weight loss and maintenance standpoint, and it gave her a good network of friends and a support group, which she especially needed now.

But trying to keep up with the program after her diagnosis—developing food plans, journaling, making phone calls, much less preparing the food—became increasingly confusing and stressful. Almost immediately after her diagnosis, she had to quit being a sponsor for others, but she wanted to try to keep up with the writing assignments, and I continued taking her to evening meetings.

Mary's sponsor, Janet, and I talked occasionally, and I began to see first-hand the burden and stress the program was causing my wife, and in turn, me. Mary had always been compulsive with respect to doing everything correctly and thoroughly. She was a real rule follower. During this time, she often fretted or worried over the possibility of doing something wrong or any perceived disappointment or disapproval by Janet (which didn't happen). She wasn't scared, per se, but she knew the program was rigid and had to be done "by the book," which she realized she could no longer handle.

Janet was understanding and allowed my wife to get by with "slips" because she knew Mary couldn't handle the program demands or any criticism from her. Eventually, Mary was technically no longer in the program. Her friends in the program allowed her to continue participating on a loose or "sliding scale" basis to provide her with friendship and give her a purpose more than anything else.

But even the HOW program came to an end. While staying in the food program, albeit unofficially, was good for Mary in some respects, the inability to cope with any rules at all caused her to stress so much that we decided it wasn't worth the anxiety anymore.

Once Mary started at Winterbrook adult day care center, she seemed to blossom again and thrive. Her time was more structured than at the senior center, the staff were actively involved with her, and a few more attendees were closer in age.

Nothing was complicated, and there were lots of activities for her to do. A bus picked her up in the morning, and I picked her up on my way home from work three days a week. Mary enjoyed being there and I didn't have to worry about her.

At Winterbrook Mary seemed to fit in and interact with others just fine. Most people had left by the time I was able to pick her up at the center after work, so I wasn't able to observe her interactions there, but when I did pop in during the day she seemed to be having a good time and the director, Barbara, always told me she was fitting in okay. Thankfully, the staff at Winterbrook were great at dealing with people in Mary's condition.

Lunch was also part of the daily routine, and since Mary had mostly given up or forgotten about her food program by this time, it was a good situation for both of us.

Still, Mary grew lonely when she was home alone on the days when she didn't go to Winterbrook or Jeff couldn't make it over. On those days I tried to keep her alone time to a minimum, and the calls with a few of her program buddies that did continue, until they dwindled down, helped a lot. I talked with her often during the workday, in addition to usually going home to make lunch and spend some time with her. Work was busy, but luckily not super busy, during this time, which allowed me to work from home on some days to stay with her.

As a couple, we had virtually no social life anymore. We went to church most Sundays, but there wasn't another couple or group who were good enough friends with whom to hang out. Thankfully, Jeff was local. Calling relatives or out of town friends on a regular basis helped, especially my mom and David, who sometimes talked with Mary several times a day when I was at work.

Trying to socialize took real effort because Mary felt uncomfortable and increasingly uneasy interacting with others, even family. Such efforts usually added more stress for both of us than it was worth.

We were mostly each other's social life, but at least we loved each other, enjoyed each other's company, and were comfortable around each other. Mary said a few times, "It's nice when you're married to your best friend."

Yet this earlier stage of progression seemed to be one of the most terrifying, because Mary was mostly aware of what was happening to her. She needed a lot of support and reassurance in many ways, not only physically to make sure tasks were done and she was well taken care of, but emotionally.

Looking back, as frustrating, time-consuming, and annoying at times as all the increased physical tasks and stresses were for me personally, it was nothing compared to the emotional strain and sadness of the situation for both of us as a couple. A cloud seemed to hover over us that kept getting darker and darker.

During this period Mary became increasingly emotional and missed our families a lot. She cried frequently, usually for no apparent reason other than out of general sadness. Often she felt she had let someone down. "I feel like I should be doing something for someone, but I don't know what," she would say, or, "I feel bad that I didn't handle that situation very well." Often she said nothing, but I could tell what she was going through by her somber silence or distressed look and general body demeanor.

Likely the worst emotional aspect for both of us was the fact Mary knew what was happening to her. She sometimes made statements like, "I don't feel like I belong," or "I feel like the world is going on around me and I'm not part of it," or "Only about half of what's happening to me seems real."

This was definitely the most heart-breaking experience for me—knowing she realized what was happening and there was nothing either of us could do to stop the progression, much less reverse it. Undoubtedly, the hardest part of it all for me was Mary not being happy.

My best ideas for how to help her came when I tried to put myself in her position and think about what would make me feel better, or at least get me through a rough moment with less anguish. If she was fretting about not doing something she thought she should be doing for someone, I said, "Let's call (the person) and see if they need anything." If she worried someone might be in trouble or need help, I suggested "Let's call them and ask how they're doing." Some type of resolution was needed to break the cycle.

I tried not to ask her to make a decision or do something with which she would have difficulty. As part of this, I distracted her if it seemed circumstances could lead down a difficult path, like if she seemed to be stuck obsessing about someone or something. For example, one time she became confused and frustrated trying to fold laundry. Rather than showing her how to do it—again—I removed the clothes from her lap and said, "Let's go make dinner."

Sometimes we would just take a drive. I pointed out beautiful scenes—rolling hills, horses in a pasture, deer grazing in a field, clouds in the sky, fall colors in the trees, or whatever was in sight—all distractions that were very meaningful to her. Seeing such "pretties" as she called them would calm her and allowed her to escape the stress, sadness and confusion, if only for a few moments. Sometimes she would even break into a "happy cry" because something was so beautiful.

She seemed to acutely focus on these types of scenes, study them, and immerse herself in them more after she was diagnosed. I remember times she stared at a sunset or sunrise until there was no more color in the sky. On summer evenings she would sit on the edge of the deck watching fireflies in amazement until they finally faded then disappeared in the black night.

While Mary had always loved these glimpses of nature, her love for and level of emotions towards them were now heightened. It was obvious she could still appreciate the pleasant parts of life without fully understanding or comprehending them. Of utmost importance was to constantly reassure her with words like, "I love you very much, I will always be with you, and we are in this together and will get through it together."

She always responded with, "Thank you. I love you too."

Often, when she couldn't think of what to say or was unable to do something, my simply saying, "It's okay," in a reassuring manner and giving her a hug was all that was needed to calm her.

My fallback position after all else failed and there was nothing I could say to help was to simply hold her in my arms and cuddle her for as long as was needed to take her back to our foundation of security and love.

During this time, all emotions, whether good or bad, were heightened, not dampened. I had heard the words "emotional roller coaster" before but had never really lived them...until now.

Chapter 7

Family Vacations

In retrospect, the two years in which Mary's disease slowly progressed after her diagnosis were definitely a "grace period" and blessing, especially since we used this time to its fullest to travel and visit family as much as we could. Our families were spread far apart, so visiting them was not simple. We lived in Maryland, as did our son Jeff, but Mary's family was in Connecticut, my family was in Texas, and David lived in Colorado. Fortunately, we were able to make at least one special trip to each family.

And some family members came to visit us. Like she had done the past several years, Mary's sister took her two-week vacation in early summer and drove to stay with us for a week, then took Mary back home with her to spend a week in Connecticut. I later drove there, stayed two days, and then brought Mary back home.

The sisters enjoyed being with each other. They went shopping, to parks, and kayaking that first year after Mary's diagnosis. Sue told me Mary seemed obsessed with flowers on some of their jaunts, picking daisies, lilies, wildflowers—whatever she would find—in state parks (even though it was illegal) and from the flower bed at Dunkin' Donuts (likely not appreciated) to take home with her. Sue was afraid they were going to get into trouble but in the long run she just let Mary do her thing. Sometimes Sue was able to explain what was acceptable to her sister, sometimes not.

Their two brothers and their families also came to Sue's house to visit. This was where all of Mary's family had gathered on special occasions for years when their parents were alive. Then the tradition continued after they passed. Of course, Mary's changing status was noticeable now. It wasn't talked about at the time, but with some relatives having had dementia, I know it had to be at least in the back of Mary's siblings' minds whether any of them would eventually suffer the same fate. Regardless, this visit was great for Sue and Mary to spend time together.

During our two trips to Texas, Mary's noticeable progression weighed especially heavy on my mother, who was ninety years old. She lived in an independent living facility where some household help was provided, but she was doing well overall. Each time she saw us, I needed to help Mary more and more, as she began to lack social skills and the organizational ability to accomplish much. Mary had always been active in the kitchen, especially since it took a lot of special preparation and weighing of food items for her program. Now I was fixing all her meals for her.

Mary was quiet sitting with my mother now because a lot of times she didn't know what to say. Thankfully, she could carry on a fairly good conversation at the time if someone else initiated it, as long as it only involved shallow talk or answering simple, specific questions. But sometimes the long gaps of silence were painful, to the point that I just couldn't take it any longer and had to chime in to relieve the awkwardness.

I'm sure some of my mother's sadness for Mary's condition was related to the fact that my father, her husband of many years, started having signs of dementia in his mid-eighties, several years before he passed away. Mom had lived with the sorrows and burdens of such a condition previously, so she knew how distressing it was. The fact that Mary was still so young, in addition to watching her son in the throes of dealing with Alzheimer's, was particularly disheartening to her.

About a year and a half after Mary was diagnosed, we visited our son David and his wife Arlyn in rural western Colorado. They lived on the side of a gently sloped mesa just outside a small town.

After our scheduled visit of about a week, I needed to return to work, but Mary really wanted to stay longer. We all agreed it would be fun and should work out well for her to stay there an extra week, which was later extended by an additional week since she was enjoying herself so much.

David called me each night to report the day's activities and how thrilled Mary was, and for the first time in a long time I was able to fall asleep peacefully knowing she was happy again.

At home she had already relinquished all kitchen and household duties to me, but on their mini-farm her engagement was renewed. She helped gather fresh fruits and vegetables from the garden, tended to the chickens, and did other "country girl" activities with them. They were able to find ways to let her help, and she absolutely loved it.

Mary was totally open to whatever they suggested, and she thoroughly enjoyed herself. They did lots of fun and silly things together, like playing frisbee on the driveway and singing a lot, even dressing up for a costume parade. They posed for funny photos, like on a tractor or while up in the air when jumping. It was a fun time for her.

David and Arlyn did a lot to make this visit special for her. They took her for a trail ride on horseback and arranged a couple of sessions working with clay on a potter's wheel. She was in heaven.

Being a multi-faceted percussionist, David had a drum-filled music room with all sorts of instruments Mary loved to play, or at least play on. They often played instruments together, or sometimes she would just sit close to him while he practiced. They had some very special times together making music. She also participated in some of the jam sessions David and Arlyn hosted. When not actively playing or singing, she blissfully smiled and swayed to the music.

Mary and I also talked on the phone every day, and she wrote a couple of short notes to me. I was told she talked about me a lot, often telling David and Arlyn how much she loved me. We used to do something silly as the boys were growing up, raising our hands and feet while driving over a cattle guard with the rumbly noise. I was told that every time they went over a cattle guard she started crying, saying, "I love Marc so much."

Arlyn's parents lived across the street. Her mother, Adrianna, took a special interest in my wife, and Mary loved doing things with her. They took lots of walks together, and she even had the patience to re-teach Mary how to crochet. Many mistakes were made, but she had fun and produced several short and wobbly scarves. She told me how relaxing it was, and no matter how the end product turned out, she was proud she could do it.

There was a dome-shaped building on Arlyn's parents' property where the family and locals often gathered for yoga, dancing, or music-making. Mary loved participating in these activities. At one session, she connected with a fluffy dog while others were dancing, lovingly holding and petting the dog for over an hour. She didn't feel the need to dance, just happy to hold the dog watching everyone else.

A few years before, Mary likely would not have felt comfortable dancing with a lot of other people or focusing on the dog so much with others around, but I came to realize that in the country, she wasn't following any rules or conditioned norms but was following her heart, reveling in the moment, the freedom to be herself no matter what that looked like. It was an epiphany for me, and I vowed to remind her in the future not to worry so much about what others thought—and to remind myself too.

Mary remained physically fit so she, David and Arlyn, took many long walks and hikes together. She loved aspen trees almost to an obsession, periodically stopping to hug one. On a three-mile loop hike in the mountains, she picked up aspen leaves all along the way to take back, gathering so many they kept falling out of her arms.

On a different day, they went to the top of Grand Mesa with its elevation of more than ten thousand feet. David told me how his mother stood on a boulder close to the edge, looked over the valley below and kept saying, "I feel like I'm standing on top of the world!"

Mary's biggest problem during her stay revolved around the fact she had little internal direction, so she needed to tether herself to someone at all times. This was reassuring to her since she didn't like to be alone. Not having someone else around was frightening to her. The problem arose during the night, while others were asleep. Mary sometimes got out of bed and ambled around the house, not knowing where people were. Luckily David was a light sleeper—undoubtedly more so while Mary was visiting—and sometimes got up and hung out with his mom for a while.

Mary had little working concept of time. One time in the middle of the night before they were scheduled to go to a yoga class at the dome the next morning, she didn't see anyone in the house when she got up and thought she was late for the class. David heard her walking around, going into every room except their bedroom. All of a sudden, he heard the outside door close and heard her running. He quickly jumped out of bed and chased after her in the dark of the night.

By the time he got outside, she was already near the end of their long driveway that went down to the road, about to cross to get to the dome. Luckily he caught up with her before she did. Mary was confused, panicked, worried she was going to miss the yoga class, but everything turned out okay. Still, it could have been a bad situation.

This episode was yet another experience reminding me I could never know with any real certainty what to expect from her with Alzheimer's.

During this visit, Mary always wanted to know what was going to happen next and what she was supposed to do. There had to be a plan for each day, for each hour. She consistently asked what they were doing or going to do if they were sitting around without a specific goal. She did this a lot at home also. David said it seemed like she realized her grip on reality was fading, so she was overcompensating to try to keep up.

Fortunately, it was harvest season, so there was much to do on their three acres. One chilly day after gardening, David went directly into the house while Arlyn and Mary passed the laundry line on the way and stopped to gather the clothes hanging there. They were wearing work gloves that had become soiled with dirt and compost. Arlyn popped off her gloves and began taking their clean laundry off the line. Mary followed her and was all excited to help.

Arlyn saw Mary was wearing her dirty gloves, so she asked Mary to take them off before handling the clean clothes. Mary was bundled up but her hands were cold even with the gloves on, apparently too cold for her to take them off. She could not be convinced that taking off the dirty gloves was needed for handling clean clothes. Arlyn then offered to get her some clean non-garden gloves to put on, but this didn't work. The emotional realm ruled supreme over the rational that day.

Mary went into the house to David, crying, "Arlyn wouldn't let me help with the laundry. She doesn't like me because she wouldn't let me help." David hugged and consoled his mom, acknowledging her feelings of helplessness and rejection. The two walked out and cleared the air with Arlyn, who assured Mary of her love, and they were able to move on to the next adventure. In retrospect, if they had a do-over, David and Arlyn said they would have let Mary help, re-washing the laundry if necessary, or simply waited for a different time to take down the clothes.

Mary could only sense the feeling of not being able to help, which went against her nature, and not the reasoning behind it—that she couldn't handle clean laundry with dirty gloves. Possibly more important to her at the time than the desire to help, was the worry that her hands would get colder, and the feeling that no one cared.

Such instances were intense for Mary at the time, but luckily were short-lived and quickly forgotten once she felt heard and comforted.

At first, David and Arlyn tried using a common-sense approach to interact with Mary, by simply communicating with her the same way they used to before she was diagnosed—like I had tried to do, failing so many times. They told me later they were glad they previously had spent time studying loving communication with each other and were able to apply those same concepts with Mary. It was a whole lot more complicated with the emotional variables Alzheimer's tossed in the mix though.

They have since had a child. David said learning how to appropriately react and connect with his mother in this manner helped him develop the skills he now uses communicating with their son…focusing on non-verbal, heart-felt communication rather than always needing and using words, staying energetically engaged despite having different truths or perceptions, and finding loving patience even when dealing with irrational fears and misunderstandings.

From the other perspective, Arlyn said she's learned a lot raising their son that she would now apply better to Mary under such circumstances. For example, a toddler has no real logic and is emotion driven. When an appropriate toy is substituted for an inappropriate item, it can't be expected for the child to understand why. Without upsetting the child unnecessarily, an adult typically can switch the items without explanation, using what a magician calls sleight of hand. Mary would sometimes pick up an item, such as a picture or cookie jar, and ask where it belonged. While the items usually went where she found them, putting them in a different spot (instead of arguing that they were right where they were supposed to be) appeased her desire to put them somewhere different. The items could later be put back in their rightful places. No harm, no foul.

Just like I've done so many times, David and Arlyn initially often tried approaching Mary rationally but to no avail, as she often couldn't relate to what was actually happening at the moment. And just like I did, they eventually realized it was easier to mimic communicating with and attending to the needs of a child when they dealt with Mary. It wasn't demeaning but practical and kept everyone relatively sane and content in the long run once you got used to it.

Mary was prepared for the trip home well in advance. She had her suitcase meticulously packed and ready to return home four days before she was to leave. She wasn't wanting to leave, but she was obsessed about missing or not being ready for something. Arlyn simply loaned her clothes so she could stay packed.

It was difficult for David to put his mother on the plane to return to Maryland, telling me it was the hardest goodbye or "see-you-later" ever.

Mary flew back to Maryland by herself, even though there were no direct flights, a choice I'd later regret. Since she would never have been able to navigate transferring from one flight to the next, the airline had someone meet and escort her between flights and put her on the plane. I was nervous about it all and didn't rest easy until I saw her walk through the gate at Dulles International Airport.

I waited for her as the passengers started streaming through the gate. Several people seemed to give me strange looks, and then a couple made comments to me like, "She'll be coming off soon," or "I think she'll be okay."

Two flight attendants flanked her through the gate, Mary and I hugged, I thanked them, and they went their way. To this day I don't know what happened on the plane, but it was definitely the last time she travelled alone. Both David and I regret not taking time off to fly with her.

I had mixed feelings while she was away this long. I missed her a lot, but I was thankful she was in good hands and was having a blast of a time she would likely never have again. We talked at least daily, so I knew she was fine and enjoying herself. Our calls were mostly lovey talk about missing each other. She also told me about all the exciting adventures she was having with David and Arlyn. I could often hear my son and his wife in the background, reminding her of the day's activities to share with me.

I have to admit I was also grateful for the opportunity to catch up on work at the office, and a lot of paperwork and cleaning that had accumulated at home that I hadn't been able to do with her around. I also caught up a little on my rest, although by then I was used to waking up quite early with Mary on my mind, rarely falling back asleep.

I think I enjoyed Mary's stay in Colorado as much as she did, knowing she was so happy. But I also realized she would probably forget the memories with her Alzheimer's. Still, I knew that at least the family would have them to hold onto in the dark times to come.

Chapter 8

Increasing Symptoms

Over time I learned that the stealthy onset of Alzheimer's is relentless. Symptoms and actions gradually became more evident over time, both in frequency and severity.

Mary's disease seemed to progress slowly during the first year following her diagnosis. During the second year, her symptoms started interfering more significantly with her functioning.

The typical early stage symptoms, similar to what she experienced for several months before her diagnosis, continued to worsen. These included general memory loss, forgetting where she put items (but now more often getting panicky about it), losing her train of thought, an inability to work the TV controls, frequently asking the day and time, and forgetting details about what was discussed with someone, or that the conversation had ever occurred.

I now sometimes saw Mary walking from room to room in our house with a worried look on her face. I could tell she was having trouble finding something the way she was looking under papers or shuffling items around on a counter or desktop.

If it seemed she was becoming frustrated, I often asked, "What are you looking for?"

Commonly she replied, "I can't find my keys," or "I'm looking for my watch," or "I don't know where I left my book." The missing items varied over time.

I often replied, "I'll help you find it."

"Thank you."

"Do you remember the last time you saw it?"

"No, it was around somewhere," she usually replied.

"Okay, let's look for it around here first, then we'll check the kitchen."

As time went on, I quit asking if she remembered the last time that she saw whatever it was that was missing since she hardly ever did, and it only brought attention to her forgetfulness.

When she entered a room but couldn't remember why, at this point I might offer a few suggestions that seemed appropriate for that room at that particular time. Sometimes this helped, sometimes it heightened her awareness of the situation. At those times, I suggested a few possible items that seemed relevant, but otherwise I tried to distract her or help her focus on something else.

Sometimes I wondered, even feared, *what if I get Alzheimer's too?* There were the times I had misplaced something. I recall when I went upstairs to our bedroom to fetch something but couldn't remember what it was upon entering the room. I told myself this was normal for someone in their sixties. It happens occasionally. *But what if...* The thought of me also getting dementia or Alzheimer's was distressing. After a while, though, I started to realize there was a big difference between her forgetfulness and mine.

She more often repeated the same question she recently asked—and I had answered shortly before. While this was annoying, especially at first, I reached the point where I simply answered the question again, in the same tone as if she had never asked it. Sometimes I answered using different words, thinking she might comprehend one response better than another. After a few times, once I realized what was happening, I never told her she had recently asked the same question.

A good example was, "What are we going to do today?"

My initial response was sometimes a question, "What would you like to do?"

After some discussion and a few minutes later, she would ask, "What are we doing today?"

"How about if we go for a drive in a little while?"

"Okay, that sounds good." And then a short time later: "What are we going to do today?"

"Let's get our coats and go for a drive," I said and retrieved our jackets and we headed out. I soon learned that saying something definitive, not in her decision realm, was needed to break the cycle, followed by an action.

If it wasn't for my overseeing everything, dirty dishes would have stacked up in the sink and the laundry would have been left in the washer for days becoming mildewed. The clothes that did make it through the dryer sometimes never got folded or were jumbled in mismatched piles so that I would either have to sort through it or start it all over again. It became much easier and less stressful—for both of us—for me to just take on these tasks myself.

The problem was that Mary still wanted to help with the chores, still wanting to be useful.

I couldn't let her cook anymore, at least unattended, for fear of her getting hurt or the house burning down, so I would let her be my sous-chef, mixing salad, or setting the table. It didn't matter to me if I had to get up and get forks to replace the spoons. I wasn't the best cook, but I learned to make do and we got carry-out on occasion.

Mary's favorite chore was doing yard work, especially mowing the lawn, but this went by the wayside quickly, much to my dismay. The last time she mowed, she stopped half-way through, leaving the mower in the middle of the yard, never to return. I came outside to find patchy strips of unmown grass in between mowed portions. She wasn't being lazy; she was just being…well, *Mary* with Alzheimer's. I'm sure the homeowners' association would have written me up for this during one of their inspections or the neighbors would soon become disgusted, so I finished it. I believe that was the last time she ever thought about mowing.

Mary often sat or stood around and did nothing if left alone. If I suggested something to her, she wouldn't know how to get started, as she couldn't initiate much on her own. She often told me, "I don't know what to do." Or she asked, "What am I supposed to do?"

I often directed her to something specific, such as, "Why don't you put away the dishes?" Or, "Can you please clean off the table?" She might start doing the task, but more often than not didn't complete it anymore. Questions like, "How about you start a load of laundry while I vacuum?" became fruitless. As time went on, she accomplished less and less even with close instructions, and I could tell any direction at all confused her and made her feel inadequate.

It was difficult, and a constant uncertainty for me, to know how much to let Mary try to do on her own or how much to ask her to help. I didn't want her to fail and thus highlight her inabilities, as this would have a negative impact on both of us. Our coordination of responsibilities transformed over time. Initially, I watched what she did and helped as necessary, becoming a second pair of hands to help her so we could accomplish the task together. I often asked, "How can I help you?" Sometimes she knew, sometimes she didn't.

The next step was me saying, "Here, let me help you," then doing what needed to be done, especially if she seemed to be having trouble with something. She was always grateful for the help with a "thank you."

Gradually taking over with her onlooking help, I started asking, "Can you help me?" I always tried to be one step ahead, so something didn't become frustrating for her. She was always close by, and she was reassured and happy just talking with me while I was busy. This worked out better for both of us.

Over time, as I slowly just took over doing everything, the incremental increases in time that each task took gradually added up and I soon had none to spare.

In the beginning, I admit I became disheartened, if not frustrated, about taking over all of the chores on top of my office workload. I guess I just needed to cut Mary some slack because she had Alzheimer's, and cut myself some slack being that I was, after all, only human. Overall, I feel I did a good job learning to "go with the flow" since there was always a new issue cropping up.

Sometimes the silence between us could be painfully awkward, at least for me. Mary often didn't seem to know what to say, so she wouldn't say anything at all. Sometimes, she said her usual, "I don't know what to do," and stood in silence, waiting for my direction. I'm sure it was uncomfortable for her too, as she had a look of uncertainty at these times, like she was trying to think of something to say but the words weren't there. At these times, I needed to be the one to start talking. The topic usually didn't make any difference, as any conversation relaxed the uneasiness…as long as it wasn't negative.

Mary always loved to read, and this would have been a good activity to keep her engaged and happy, but sadly, her ability to concentrate enough on the words before her declined quickly. Still, sometimes when it appeared she wanted something to do, I asked, "Would you like to read more in this book you started?" physically handing her the book open to the page where her marker was previously inserted.

"I don't know," she would reply.

"Well, why don't you sit here and try it. You always enjoyed reading books like this, so I think you'll like it."

She might try reading for a few minutes, or she might just hold the book for a short time before putting it down. I didn't continue trying this once I realized she really couldn't do it, as opposed to just not being "in the mood."

Church also became difficult over time since Mary started needing help finding books in the Bible, not simply passages, which became a distraction not only to me but others sitting nearby. It just became more difficult to go than not, but we continued to go, partially for the social interactions.

Mary had always been easy going before her Alzheimer's took hold. Two years in I started to notice she would become upset for no reason. I would ask why but she couldn't answer. She simply didn't know why. I'm sure this tied in with the times she had an uneasy feeling that she needed to do something or be somewhere, or like she was letting someone down by not doing something—she just didn't know what or who it was. This led to her being worried and feeling guilty, often saying, "I feel like I need to be helping someone," in a worried tone.

I would ask, "Do you know who?"

"No, but I know it's someone," she might reply.

I would try to offer a specific suggestion at times. "Do you want to call your HOW friends Diana or Vicki to see if they need help?" I would ask. Sometimes she called, sometimes she didn't.

It was often difficult to assess how much of her general confusion was a direct result of memory loss and forgetfulness versus a general muddled or disconnected state not directly related to being unable to remember something correctly. Practically, it really didn't make any difference whether she couldn't remember what to do or if she was just confused— either was an acutely disturbing experience to her and affected what she was able to do and how she functioned in all aspects of her life. I'm sure for her it was like being on a never-ending merry-go-round…no beginning, no end.

As her disease progressed, my wife became more confused overall, generally lost concentration and focus, and had trouble doing even simple tasks or following any directions or instructions. She became concerned or sometimes panicky when something was upsetting. I think that at times when she didn't know what to do, she couldn't put into perspective the seriousness (or lack of it) of not doing it, so all such instances were viewed with a heightened urgency.

If she became upset over something, this made her more frazzled, which aggravated the situation. The best solution over time for me was to keep the overall atmosphere as calm and non-threatening as possible, which meant I gradually took over helping her with all of her normal tasks, holding back a lot of things I might normally have said or was thinking.

While she must have felt like a mouse stuck in a maze, I felt like I was in a mousetrap, the homemade kind where there was a box over me, with no room to run or hide and no one to hear me, with tiny airholes letting in just enough air to breathe, but very little sunshine.

Mary became somewhat of a compulsive shopper, at least for certain things. Whether this was due to a change in her emotional state, forgetting she already had a lot of a particular item, a decrease in inhibitions, or was a prelude of what was to come is uncertain.

Sometimes in a store, she saw something she wanted though she already had several of them. She sometimes became upset or pouted in the store if I tried too hard to convince her she didn't need something, and occasionally she started to make a scene, arguing louder and louder until I gave in to her whims, like a father to his child who started to throw a temper tantrum. After a couple of minor scenes, I learned to let her have what she wanted, and we ended up with a lot of never used items: we had many purses, gloves, socks, hair clips, reading magnification glasses, Christmas ornaments, pens, pencils...which I never got rid of while she was around but eventually became charity donations. I was likely too lenient with letting her buy so much, but it made her happy at the time—plus, it circumvented any confrontation, which was important for both of our sakes.

From a shopping standpoint, it was hard not to get impatient at times. I sometimes became annoyed in a store, but at least I learned over time not to show it. Mary often didn't realize what she was doing and couldn't control her impulses, and my getting upset usually only worsened the situation.

The biggest shopping "killer" came while we stood in line waiting for an available cashier. There they sat, all those shelves of goods, alluring someone to make a last-minute impulse buy. No doubt it's intentional there are never enough cashiers available, so customers have plenty of time to view all those enticing items. And Mary was a perfect target! With all the possibilities, how could she not find something she "needed."

In hindsight, I'm not sure how I would have handled these situations differently under the circumstances, as I was trying to let her be as happy as possible for as long as possible. Plus, I didn't want to cause discord between us over something insignificant. None of the items Mary wanted were expensive, and the amount of money involved wasn't an issue—it was more aggravating to my frugalness, okay cheapness, than anything else.

One of the most obvious general changes over time affecting all aspects of her functioning and our lives was that her organizational skills kept diminishing. This resulted in a lot of nonproductive puttering, where she often "reorganized" items by moving them around for no reason, usually on her desk or kitchen or bathroom counters—almost anywhere there were a number of things. Of course, this meant we were constantly searching for things. Trying to find small items like keys or remote controls became time consuming.

Obviously, there was a need to de-clutter and organize so that Mary could find and access the things she needed each day. I realized belatedly that the time to do such organizing would have been long before Mary's disease started progressing. We were never good about getting rid of belongings if we never used them any longer.

Each time we moved, most of the old possessions were packed, or sometimes were still packed from the previous move, to take with us to our newest home. This packrat mentality was detrimental in a number of ways over the years, but certainly hit a high point—or low point—with Mary's issues. This was a great lesson learned, but too late for us.

However, after a little trial and error, I did eventually learn to help my wife decide on what to wear each day. With Mary being at different weights over the years, and especially with her loving to shop in the petite section to reward herself, she had accumulated many clothes. This had its drawbacks, as I sometimes found her standing in her closet in the morning, completely overwhelmed by what to wear. How could she choose from all those possibilities? The best way to circumvent this was for me to pick out a couple of choices I knew she liked and were appropriate for the day, and ask her, "Which one do you want to wear?" usually outside the closet so as not to confuse the options. If she was still indecisive, I often presented one and said, "How about this one? It looks very nice on you." Rarely was there ever any questioning.

One of the initial and most noticeable difficulties for Mary was that she had little concept of time. She hardly ever knew what day it was and quickly came to the point when she couldn't tell time, whether on a digital or regular clock, much less put the time in context with what needed to be done. I tried instructing her on how to tell time, but this was frustrating for both of us at this stage. I needed to be specific and tell her when something needed to be accomplished or a call needed to be made. Setting a timer with a note beside it worked to some degree at first.

In retrospect, I shouldn't have been surprised with her trouble telling time. During the clinical trial, at several visits she was asked to draw the face of a clock, placing the twelve hours in the correct place. If the face was reasonable, she was asked to draw in the hands at a stated time. I could see over the months she was assessed how this ability declined.

With her special food program, she called her sponsor at a specified time every morning. She usually arose from bed early so she didn't miss making the call. She often sat at our kitchen table for over thirty minutes, intently watching the clock in front of her or for the timer to ring, holding the phone with her thumb on the button for the first number to dial so she wasn't late. Sometimes I told her, "You know you're not supposed to call Janet for another thirty minutes."

She replied, "I know, but I don't want to miss calling her on time. She's scheduled this time for me, and I need to honor it." More than once she got out of bed in the middle of the night, picking up the phone, thinking she needed to make the call. My setting an alarm helped a little, but she still often waited, holding the phone.

Over time, Mary started sleeping less, waking up more during the night. A few times I woke up and she wasn't in bed. Of course, this was scary. If she wasn't in the bathroom, she was downstairs. I don't believe she ever wandered outside at night… that I know of. If I had thought about it at the time, I might have changed the outside door locks so these doors couldn't be opened from the inside without a key, but this could be a potential safety concern on its own.

I distinctly remember one night she woke up and sat up quickly. "Oh my gosh, it's twelve…fifty-three," she said, reading the digital clock numbers. What am I going to do?" She jumped out of bed, went downstairs, and brought up her food plan and writing assignment for the next day for me to check over again, which I did, and she went back downstairs. When she didn't return after a while, I went downstairs, and she was sitting at the kitchen table with phone in hand.

I asked, "What are you doing down here at this time of the night?"

"I'm waiting to call Janet."

"You don't need to call her until eight-fifteen. It's only one-thirty…*in the morning*." I tried not to sound as unnerved as I felt.

"I don't want to miss it."

I told her, "That's a long time away. I've set an alarm so you won't miss it. Let's go set a second alarm in case the first one doesn't work." She seemed unconvinced. So I gently took the phone from her hand, held both of her hands to help her up, and said, "Come on. Let's go upstairs. We'll put the phone close to you on the headboard, so you'll have it right there when the alarm rings." Reluctantly, she came back up to bed.

Mary thought less and less about good hygiene. I made sure she washed her hands well before helping to prepare food or eating, or after toileting. I initially watched to make sure she washed adequately, but the point arrived where I needed to help her.

She didn't seem to think about taking baths and often didn't want to. She rarely did anything active or dirty during this later time, so I let her go for several days without a full bath. This was one of those times to pick my battles. It wasn't worth an argument or making her feel bad or inadequate if something wasn't necessary. To circumvent the issue, I sometimes took her in the shower with me, but she fainted a couple of times, likely from standing in the heat too long, so this was short-lived.

Dental hygiene was somewhat difficult. Mary often forgot to brush her teeth or felt it wasn't important when I reminded her. She previously had some gum problems and was susceptible to gingivitis, so this was not something I could let slide. I definitely needed to stay on top of this and help her brush and floss on a regular basis, which she generally let me do.

Toileting was another function to keep under surveillance. I could handle reminding her to wash her hands or flush the toilet. Reminding her what she needed to do while on the toilet was a different story. She could recognize the urge, although I reminded her to go before we went anywhere. A few times she was confused about what to do once she finished. In such cases, I reminded her what needed to be done or helped her as necessary. Thankfully, she almost always seemed grateful, or at least indifferent and not resistant, to my helping her during this period in all aspects.

When something wasn't done correctly, whether toileting or otherwise, she often thought she was actually helping by what she was doing wrong. My getting upset or chastising her certainly wasn't appropriate, but gentle reminders of what to do seemed to be the best option without making a big deal about it.

Mary was good about taking her medications during most of this two-year period, but of course she had to be reminded to take them more and more often, and eventually I needed to hand them to her. I usually gave her a chance to take them on her own with a reminder. A routine of taking medications and brushing teeth at the same time worked the best.

Allocating all her medications ahead of time into morning and evening compartments helped a lot, especially when we were traveling. Putting a complete supply together for any time I wasn't with her was a total necessity, and whoever she was staying with needed to know the routine. But this was rare and only with close family. It was good to have a week or more in compartments in advance, as well as a note stating which medications needed to be taken at what time, in the event someone else had to unexpectedly replace me or watch over her.

Safety was not a significant problem yet, but there were a few episodes. Occasionally she would fail to turn on or off the right burners on the stove, lock doors when she went for a walk with Cody, or close the garage door while she was still driving. None of these times of negligence on her part ever caused a problem for us, but they certainly could have. Thankfully, she never wandered outside the house.

Mary's driving privileges, of course, had to be curtailed and then revoked when the disease progressed to the point where she could no longer follow directions or instructions. As much as I wanted to allow my wife her freedom, I recognized that it could be dangerous if she became lost, if she got stuck in traffic, if she had to react quickly in a situation, or if she wasn't cognizant of everything happening around her. Mary was able to drive to nearby, familiar places for several months after her diagnosis, like the senior center, but it came to the point where it wouldn't be safe. She wanted to drive and having to give up this freedom was an issue that caused a few arguments between us at times—yet, unlike the shopping sprees, I had to put my foot down on this one.

Luckily the driving debates didn't last too long. As a precaution, I made sure car keys weren't readily accessible. I've always done most of the driving throughout the years, so we usually took my car and it was expected I would drive.

While this plan with my doing most of the driving generally worked well for us, it would have been tremendously difficult and upsetting for both of us if I was the affected person and Mary had to do all the driving. My wife was never a confident driver, and she realized it. She never drove on Interstates or in confusing areas with lots of traffic or where quick decisions needed to be made, especially while trying to read road signs. Her driving was always local or familiar. Still, I could see Alzheimer's took her doubts and fears to a whole new level where driving would have been not only dangerous for her but for others on the road.

With her memory and orientation issues, there were several times when she told me that I was going the wrong way when I was driving—which means she would have definitely gone the wrong way if she was driving.

Mary's maintaining a healthy diet undoubtedly worked in her favor, but it was more complicated because she was on a rigorous food plan that was not easy to follow even in the best of times. The food program had always required a lot of time with planning what she was going to eat a day ahead of time, as well as reading assignments and writing about how the readings applied to or affected her life, plus being on calls both with her sponsor and as a sponsor for others.

I had transitioned to taking the lead role for preparing meals and letting her help, but ultimately I ended up taking food preparation over fully. I tried to stick with her strict food plan as best as I could, but her condition advanced to the point where she couldn't understand the details of her plan and ate extra items that weren't on it—again, a topic not worth fighting over. On the bright side, she always appreciated that I cooked and almost always told me, "I like it. Thank you." Her stating or showing appreciation went a long way.

One habit Mary developed was to start eating the moment that food was placed in front of her. It was there, and she didn't think about waiting for others. To circumvent this, I simply started putting everyone's food on the table at the same time. I found that some annoying mannerisms, such as this one, have simple fixes.

Her eating techniques also changed some during this time with respect to using proper utensils. For example, I recall her trying to eat soup with a fork or using a spoon for items on a plate normally eaten with a fork. I handed her a spoon for the soup, but these types of missteps didn't make any difference, and we never ate in a more formal setting. During this time, family understood, as did most others once the situation was explained—not in Mary's presence of course.

I tried to be tolerant, and, over time, I feel I became rather decent at dealing with her disease, accepting each situation as it was, developing unique instructions or rules for Mary, and showing the appropriate reactions, at least most of the time.

We found a way to make it work, for both of us, as best as we could under the circumstances. I discovered it was much better to focus on our present situation as opposed to thinking about how much better our lives were in the past or anticipating what our future might or might not hold.

For the most part, Mary knew what was happening to her, and she seemed to greatly appreciate what I did for her during this time. She also seemed to realize the extra burden her Alzheimer's was putting on me and felt guilty about it, but she understood enough to know this was the way it needed to be. She often told me, "Thank you," both for specific tasks I did and in general.

Our best times were when I asked her to help me and we were a part of each other's lives, whether she could help in a productive manner or not. Often, we simply did lovey things like sitting on the sofa with my arm around her or standing together and hugging. She had always been a touchy-feely sort of person, and this connected with her. We seemed to be able to find ways to enjoy, or at least endure, how situations presented themselves, no matter how far they were from the ideal or how we would rather they be.

Still, I was starting to reach a point where endurance wasn't enough, where I felt constantly worn out and isolated, so I started attending a support group run by the Alzheimer's Association. Mary was supportive of this and understood. She had attended support groups of different types, and she encouraged me to participate, though I could tell the fact that I needed to go to such a group because of her distressed her.

This support group met monthly, with a facilitator provided by the Alzheimer's Association. Occasionally there was a speaker, but the usual meetings revolved around people sharing their situations and others providing helpful suggestions when possible.

Everyone who attended had their own stories to tell and challenges to face, and they were all stressed about their loved ones because they were in the middle of dealing with their own bad situations. Listening to others' stories and circumstances was disheartening but helpful in several ways—it let me know I wasn't alone through this ordeal, and it provided some ideas for how to cope with what might happen in the future. Even though I thought I was far from needing home care or a residence for Mary, I learned about the various possibilities for them in case the time came.

In hearing others' stories, I found that things could always be worse, which, of course, could be encouraging or discouraging, depending on the day. But I always left feeling a little less depressed about my current situation and more prepared to make the best of it. Our discussions showed me there were a variety of Alzheimer's and dementia types, all having similarities but with potentially very different symptoms and sometimes treatments.

The most important thing I learned was that what works for one patient in a particular circumstance doesn't necessarily work for another. One member of the group always told new people, "Once you've met one Alzheimer's patient...you've met one Alzheimer's patient," emphasizing the fact that everyone has a different journey.

My first meeting I'm sure I looked like a lot of new people I started to see now that I had been attending for a while—with that "deer-in-the-headlights" look—because I felt so overwhelmed and didn't know where to begin or what to expect.

After a few meetings, sharing my story and my problems, I started to feel my tension ease a bit, knowing there were others who could relate and maybe even offer solutions, or at least suggestions. Knowing what to expect ahead of time was a good thing, even though it was kind of scary. And over time it felt good when I could share some of my lessons learned from dealing with Mary, especially when newbies showed up with that same dazed look.

But no one at any of the meetings I attended prepared me for what I was to experience next.

Chapter 9

Where Did My Wife Go?

Mary's diagnosis was depressing enough, but her escalating progression with decreased memory, functional abilities, social skills, and overall cognition was deeply disturbing to both of us.

To make matters worse, a little over two years after Mary was diagnosed, she developed a strange illness saying she had headaches, intestinal pain with "gurgles" and some nausea. She generally felt overly tired and wanted to be in bed most of the time.

At the beginning of this illness, she said, "I've never been this sick before."

I told her, "I'll call your primary doctor and make whatever appointments are necessary."

About a week into it, she said, "I'm very worried something else is going on."

"Can you tell me what it feels like?"

"I'm very tired and just want to lie down and sleep. I have a headache. My tummy hurts. I feel different than I ever have before. I don't know what's happening to me, but it's bad." She couldn't explain her strange feelings any further at the time, but little did she know how right she was.

She had been attending Winterbrook several days a week up until this time, but she was now too ill to go, and she certainly couldn't handle it in this condition.

I took her to various doctors several times, including her primary care physician, gynecologist, and gastroenterologist. Mary's mother had emphysema, and now Mary was convinced she had developed it and was dying because of it, though there were no symptoms or chest x-ray findings. I was also in contact with the neurology group at the Georgetown research center where she participated in the clinical study, as they were still following her regarding medication for her Alzheimer's.

Nothing seemed to help, and no one could find anything wrong. The only abnormality anyone could find was a somewhat low vitamin D level. Initially, she didn't have a urinary tract infection, which often aggravates Alzheimer's symptoms. A migraine medication was prescribed for the headaches, but this didn't seem to help much, if any. Her Alzheimer's medication had recently been switched from Aricept 10 mg to Aricept 23 mg extended release. The neurologist's office said this could affect the gastrointestinal system and cause some general malaise, so she was changed back to the 10 mg dose. Towards the later part of this time she was prescribed an antibiotic for a urinary tract infection that now tested positive.

I stayed home with her many days. Thankfully, my work at this time was flexible enough for me to work from home a good part of the time. On days I had to go into the office, I came home and fixed lunch for her, stayed a while, and then returned home as early as possible at the end of my workday. She was in bed virtually the whole day whether I was there or not. At first, at least outwardly, it didn't seem any different than her not feeling well and being extremely tired, like having a bad case of the flu but without the fever.

After a couple of weeks, she wasn't so tired all the time and didn't seem to be as sick, although she still complained occasionally of intestinal pain and her head sometimes hurt. But while she became physically better, this acute illness was the start of a downhill spiral during which numerous fears and psychiatric manifestations became obvious, and new "events" started.

The next three months were truly bizarre and distressful for both of us. Neither of us could have ever envisioned in our wildest dreams what was about to transpire during this time.

One of the earliest episodes indicating something more significant was wrong occurred when Jeff and I were at home with Mary. For no apparent reason, she grew frantic, ranting, "We have no money."

I told her, "Don't worry about that. We have plenty of money."

She wouldn't believe me and said, "No we don't. We have no money."

I went upstairs and brought down the latest bank statement. I pointed to the number showing our current balance and said, "See, that's the amount of money we have in the bank, so there's nothing to worry about."

She still wouldn't believe me and said, "You're wrong, and that statement is wrong. We're broke."

I became frustrated and upset, thinking, *the facts are right in front of her—how can she be so illogical?*

I came up with the brilliant idea of taking her to the bank where both of us could ask for the balance in our checking account so she would have no more doubts.

Once at the bank, Mary calmed down some but remained agitated. When it was our turn, we walked up to the teller. I entered our bank card and security information, after which the teller asked nicely, "How may I help you?" of course having no idea of Mary's and my previous conversation.

"Can you please give us a printout of how much money we have in our checking account?" I asked.

Upon receiving the statement, I pointed out the balance amount to Mary and said, in an assuring tone, "See, we have plenty of money in the bank."

She wouldn't believe it. "No, that's not right."

I asked the teller in front of Mary, "Are you sure we have this much money?"

The teller assured us we did, but Mary still didn't believe it. She started to make a scene, telling everyone at the bank in a loud voice, "We have no money. We're broke. What are we going to do?"

Of course, this attracted everyone's attention and they were staring at us. At that point, all I wanted to do was leave quickly, discretely mouthing "sorry" to the other people in line as we hurried past them.

My nature, as a scientist by training, has always been to think through a problem logically in a step-by-step process. As a result, I often tried to talk Mary through a situation in a logical manner, presenting the facts, such as taking her to the bank to prove my point. I'm apparently a slow learner, since it took me several such blunders to realize using logic wouldn't work and might only make the situation worse, whatever it was at the time. After the bank episode wounding, I quickly learned not to take her to a public place to try to make a point.

Towards the end of her acute illness, Mary told me, "I feel like I'm becoming dissociative." Another time she said, "I feel I'm beginning to dissociate."

She had never had any such problems previously, and I didn't whole-heartedly take her seriously at first since at times some of what she said at this point didn't make sense. However, she had helped some friends in the past who were dissociative, so she knew what it meant. She sensed it, and stated, "Something is coming on. I want to feel like my old self again." She knew what was happening, or at least that she was taking a turn for the worse. This was difficult emotionally for both of us.

Having previously discussed with her some of the problems her dissociative friends exhibited, I was familiar with "disassociation" to some degree. I understood enough to know it was a mental process in which people disconnected or "detached" from their thoughts, emotions, or sense of identity. I had actually observed on several occasions how her friends took on a different identity or personality.

One Saturday morning while I was standing at our bathroom vanity shaving, Mary walked up to me in quick, bouncy steps full of energy. She was smiling, her eyes were wide-open and bright, and there was a lot of expression in her face and voice. She said, "Hi," in a perky voice.

"Hi." I smiled back, glad to see she was feeling better, cheerful even, yet wondering what had changed.

She asked, "Who are you?"

"I'm Marc," I replied, thinking she had just forgotten my name due to the Alzheimer's, not yet realizing something was significantly different.

"Where do you live?"

"I live here in this house."

"That's nice," she replied.

There was a short pause while I was processing this exchange, after which I asked, "Where do you live?"

"I don't know. I'm just a little girl." She scurried off giggling. I stood dumbfounded, not knowing what to think except, *who was that and what just happened?* I went downstairs shortly afterward, and she seemed her normal self again.

Sadly, I was soon to discover that Mary had signs of Dissociative Identity Disorder (previously termed Multiple Personality Disorder), which I later found out was often the result of an overwhelming traumatic experience or abuse that had occurred in childhood. Although this was not an official diagnosis, I observed that Mary exhibited various "identities" or "personalities"—at least four that I witnessed in a short period of time.

The youngest identity, and the first one that noticeably surfaced, was the little girl, likely about five years old. A few times, Mary said, "I'm just a little girl," and she talked with the mannerisms and innocence of a young girl. The tone and style of her voice changed to reflect this. She often called me "Mr. Marc" or "Uncle Marc," sometimes also calling our sons "uncle."

When this identity was present, we had nice talks and I could make her feel secure. She was easy to talk with, and she loved holding and talking to stuffed animals, as well as sometimes watching cartoons.

She often told me, "You're a nice man." This version of Mary usually bore no perceived relationship to me. However, she sometimes woke up in the morning thinking I was her "daddy." She was scared but happy that I loved and protected her. She loved cuddling and being held tightly during these times.

Sometimes she asked, "Where's mommy?" This was her reality at the time, so I felt I needed to play along and not approach it logically.

Initially I didn't know what the best response would be, so I told her, "Mommy's not here right now but will be back shortly."

To this, she usually responded, "Oh," or "Okay," in a disappointed voice. Sometimes she asked, "When will she be back?"

At this, I usually replied, "She'll be back in just a little while."

After a few times I learned what worked best. I told her, "Mommy's out helping someone and will be back in a little while."

Little Mary liked to hear this and always showed a proud smile, saying, "That's nice. Mommy always likes to help people." This usually settled her questions for a while.

The best way for me to respond to such circumstances in general was to do so in a calming manner, trying to think of something likely to make sense and that might be expected from a "mommy" or whoever was being asked about, which was not always readily apparent as she sometimes asked about someone other than "mommy."

Once she asked, "What's my name?"

I told her, "Your name is Mary."

She smiled and asked, "What's my mommy's name?"

"Your mommy's name is Mary also." She beamed and became all excited she was named after mommy.

At times, Mary realized she was dissociating to a child and claimed once this little girl had gone through a horrifying experience in a closet. She couldn't provide any details but was truly scared and wanted to get rid of all closets. I started closing all of the closet doors in the house which seemed to help.

There were many times she didn't know who I was much less my name. One time, after she asked my name and I told her it was Marc, she looked at me inquisitively and repeated, "*What's* your name?" in a more doubtful manner.

I told her again, "My name is Marc," but it didn't register.

So she seemed to switch tactics and asked, "How long have you known me?"

I told her, "I've known you for thirty-five years."

"I'm not that old," she said, pouting. "And I don't talk to strangers." She made a swift turnaround and scampered away.

Sometimes Mary took on the identity of a child a bit older—a preteen maybe about twelve years of age. I know this because Mary said, "There's another person with me (meaning inside my mind) who's an adolescent." During some of these times she seemed to realize both an adult and an adolescent were present at the same time, and she could somehow distinguish between the two. Except for the frightening closet revelation, when she was a five-year-old, it seemed only the child was present and no one else.

Mary's adolescent was more "flighty" than her adult identity and sometimes had an attitude often expected from a teenager. She became a little flip at times, once defiantly saying, "I don't have to listen to you," then quickly walking away.

I can't say she was more dramatic with this identity, as she was usually emotional during this period in one way or another, but she did exhibit a teen attitude. It seemed she was trying to be more independent and not as clingy as the little girl.

The next persona Mary exhibited seemed about thirty years old. She once said, "I'm worried about our little girl," which, of course, we didn't have. This one had a young adult personality that was different from the others.

I believe it was while she was in this identity that she often looked at herself in the mirror for a long time and said, "Interesting, I never knew what I looked like before." She smiled and seemed pleased with the way she looked, sometimes tilting her face or shifting her body for a different view.

While it could have been due to some completely separate underlying psychiatric problem going on, it seemed this identity had a new friend she talked to in the mirror. She would talk to the image softly and I usually couldn't understand what was being said, but she was smiling and obviously enjoying the talk. A couple of times I understood. "You're a good girl," I heard her say.

I didn't know how to address the person in the mirror, or if I even should. I was initially shocked by it, but with everything else going on I don't know why this would surprise me. I never directly addressed the person in the mirror, as I thought Mary would let me know somehow if it was appropriate for me to interact with or acknowledge her. This was Mary's friend, and she was happy talking to her. With all of the confusing changes occurring I didn't want to disrupt this peaceful time. I believe the only time I said something to Mary related to this was, "That's nice, you have a friend." This was simple, pleasant, and noncommittal.

Occasionally Mary would apparently lose sight of her imaginary friend asking, "Where did she go?" We would go looking for her together until she was distracted by something—or *someone*—else. Sometimes she was concerned about a missing little girl, saying, "I'm very worried."

"Why?" I asked, at least the first few times.

"There's a little girl missing, and I think she might be hurt or in trouble."

"What makes you think so?"

"I don't know. I just know she is. We need to help find her."

"Okay, let's take a walk around the neighborhood to see if we see her." Or sometimes I'd reply, "Then let's take a drive to see if we can find her."

"Thank you. Let's hurry." And off we went for our walk or drive. She became less worried the longer we were away and eventually dropped it, but sometimes we talked about going back out again later to look for her.

The fourth identity to surface seemed to be a woman in her mid-forties, maybe fifteen years younger than Mary's actual age. This person knew her name was Mary. One time I asked her how old she was, and she stated she was forty-five. This slightly younger Mary seemed rational and could be talked with reasonably, but she surfaced and was identifiable only a few times from what I could tell. She was like the normal and logical Mary at that time of her life. This was a nice identity to talk to because she seemed coherent and didn't know about all the problems we were having. She brought back good memories. This personality was not the real Mary, but I liked her as she was always in a more lucid and happier state.

Then there was the real Mary, the current sixty-two-year-old, but considerably different from the way she'd been before the illness. This Mary was the most difficult personality, of course the only "real" person, and sadly the hardest with whom to live.

There may have been other identities who presented themselves from time to time, but it's difficult to say as they were quite likely different presentations of one of the four, or just Mary with Alzheimer's, depending on the circumstances.

There were also other individuals named Mary who she talked about, all imagined but real to her. There was an evil sister who allegedly tampered with both of our medications, a friend in need who Mary wanted to help, and a nice person who was away on a trip for a while to meet with some old friends and help people—all named Mary. She liked and identified with this last Mary, likely because this was her true nature. She spoke proudly about being a friend of this one.

It was not uncommon for her to talk about "Mary" in the third person. I often couldn't tell which Mary she was referring to, so I needed to approach each encounter cautiously and try to choose my words wisely. At times, she said, "I'm worried about Mary. I hope she's okay. I'm going upstairs to check on her."

Once she returned, I never knew if I should ask about "Mary" or not. One time I asked, "Is Mary okay?" and she answered, "She wasn't there, but I'm still worried. I'll check again later."

With all the different identities and variations within each one, the others named Mary plus the real Mary, it was impossible to know who or what to expect or how to react minute to minute, since the various personalities fluctuated so suddenly and each needed to be responded to differently. It was an interesting time to say the least! I felt like we were continually walking along a cliff, not knowing if I might say the wrong thing to the wrong "person" to push her over the edge. At the time, I just tried to prepare to take care of all of them and not ask too many questions that might inflame any of them or, God forbid, bring another identity to the surface.

While the entire experience was difficult and trying for me, it must have been terrifying for Mary, especially since at times she realized she was dissociating. Maybe these different identities were the result of some repressed and thus long-forgotten trauma during childhood that now became exposed, as is known to be a cause of such dissociative problems later in life. During her acute illness she was often in a half-awake/half-asleep state, possibly blurring her ability to discern dreams from reality, but of course this will never be known. Possibly this explains why she became so afraid of the house, especially closets.

Maybe thinking she was dying of emphysema was partially denial, a "diversion" from having Alzheimer's. At the time, she sometimes even thought I was the one with Alzheimer's, so maybe she was trying to transfer her cognitive impairment issues onto me because she couldn't cope with them. Maybe it was due to complications of Alzheimer's that will never be understood. Whatever the underlying problem, *everyone* needed to be addressed carefully. I look back now and try to tell myself I did the best I could at the time living with a house full of people who could inexplicably and interchangeably show up at a moment's notice.

The different identities had started developing at the end of her acute illness and surfaced over the next two months. A couple of the identities seemed to dissipate, but at least the little girl and the one who seemed obsessed with looking at herself in the mirror continued to pop up throughout this time, and even beyond.

Toward the end of this time, Mary was in a little girl state more often. One time when she was in this identity, she recounted how she was scared while she was growing up and would go hide in the furthest corner of the house. I could never tell if this was all in her imagination, possibly repressed memories coming to the surface, or exaggerations of the past. Mary had never eluded to any such incidents before now, and there was now no way to find out what might have happened. It profoundly distressed me that she might have suffered through such a horrendous ordeal growing up.

If only these identities were the worst of it all though…

Chapter 10

Fears and Delusions

In addition to Mary's multiple identities, a combination of other psychiatric-related phenomena started at the same time that complicated her life and mine even more. Mary was fearful most of the time toward the end of her acute illness, especially around our house. She also started exhibiting delusions—false beliefs I couldn't change, regardless of what I told her or showed her to be true. Her fears and delusions often overlapped, and it was difficult to separate the two, if indeed they were separable.

Several times she asked, "How do I know there's not someone hiding under that pile of clothes?" eyeing it with a concerned look as we passed by.

I told her, "There's no way anyone could be hiding there, but let's check it out to be sure." I moved items around to show her—yes, actually trying to logically prove to her—that no one was there or could be there, but there were renewed fears on an ongoing basis.

She sometimes thought someone else was in our home, so I needed to check out the whole house for her. If she thought someone or something was in the attic above our bedroom, I needed to get a ladder, open the hatch in the top of my closet, and look around with a flashlight for her to believe it was okay, but usually even that didn't appease her. Her fearfulness escalated over time.

She became overly afraid of noises, almost any. Not only did she think there might be someone else in the house or attic when she heard something, but at times she thought there was a demonic presence in the closet, attic, or house in general. She thought someone—or something—could be in the air vents. She was scared when airplanes flew overhead, intently looking up at them and saying, "That's not right."

She often talked about, and was worried about, people being behind the wall in her closet. She told me, "There are children being tortured in the walls." She was extremely concerned about others and thought people were getting hurt, especially little girls under different circumstances.

I tried to explain from a logical standpoint, "There is no way anyone could be behind the walls," adding at times, "especially since they are outside walls and there's not enough room for anyone to fit there." It was worth a try but, of course, this did no good.

She continued to be afraid of closets most of the time, though I now kept the doors closed. She was sometimes fearful of going upstairs alone, thinking someone might jump out and snatch her. This overall fearfulness may have driven her to need the identity of the young child who could sense security from a protective father, but of course there's no way to know if they were related or which came first.

She didn't want to be left alone because she was afraid of so many potential, terrible possibilities around the house. During this time, she was never left alone. Between Jeff, David, Sue, and me we made sure someone was always with her. She even agreed to go back to the adult day care center for a while, but after a few times she refused to go anymore, and was eventually in no condition to return because of her fears, delusions and multiple identities.

Mary usually didn't sleep well, or she woke up too early in the morning, or both. She often touched me on my shoulder during the night, waking me up to make sure I was still there for her. She wanted to talk a lot at night and early in the morning, and she often cried. I constantly consoled her as best I could. She loved it when we cuddled, which seemed to provide her with immediate protection and general reassurance I was with her.

Her dreams or imaginations seemed more real to her, sometimes to the point she might not know if something was a reality or not.

She woke me up a good bit thinking someone was in the house, the sleeping dog needed to go outside, a car was parked in front of the house (which she thought she knew without looking), or she thought she heard something. The following scenario was not uncommon.

"Marc, Marc! Wake up."

"Hmmm." Groaning groggily was the one response I could muster at the time.

"Marc, there's someone in the house."

"Huh?"

"There's someone downstairs, and you need to go check it out."

"Okay, I'll go check. You wait here."

The first few times this happened I jumped out of bed quickly, grabbed a flashlight and something that could be used as a weapon, and cautiously and thoroughly looked in every nook and cranny of the house. Of course, my activities always started Cody barking. Coming back a while later, after checking all the bedrooms, each room downstairs, the basement, the garage, and looking out several doors and windows, I returned to where she was sitting anxiously in bed. "I checked out the whole house and there's no one there. Everything is fine and we're safe." This appeased her for a while.

I was wide awake from this quest now, my adrenaline pumping, fearful that someone might actually be lurking in our house.

After several such episodes, I didn't respond or get up quite as quickly as Mary thought I should, so she added, "Do you want people to get hurt? It'll be your fault if someone gets hurt." Of course, this laid on the guilt, plus I knew she wouldn't let me try to fall back asleep until everything was thoroughly resolved, so onward I went and usually failed to fall back to sleep.

She more and more often woke me from a dead sleep in a frantic mode, insisting I check out the house several times in search of an imaginary person she claimed was there. Needless to say, I didn't get enough sleep, plus I started sleeping lighter, which of course added to my stress. Similar instances during the night occasionally had occurred previously before her illness, but it now happened almost every night, and her concerns were much more serious and needed immediate attention.

During David's visit, Mary told me, "I'm very concerned about David. The angel Gabriel has given David to me as my 'charge' to protect him and his soul." I looked at her and couldn't think of anything to say, so she continued, "I know fulfilling this charge will be more difficult since I've been dissociative, so I'm going to need your help." She realized, at least to some extent, what was happening to her.

I still didn't have a good response, except to say, "I know this will be a big responsibility, so I'll help you anyway I can." Based on experience, I knew that this was a time when questioning her would only thwart the conversation.

This topic continued on several occasions, with Mary saying, "I feel like there's high-powered spiritual warfare going on over David. There's an 'interloper' (who in this case was a demonic spiritual being) trying to take David away from us." On another occasion, "The interloper is trying to corrupt David and take my place in David's life as his mother."

Several instances of this came into play when she was with David, and there was no room for discussion. Mary was afraid David would never return for another visit because the interloper would get in the way and steal his soul. Her belief she was losing David was difficult to deal with and impossible to discuss.

During David's visit, Mary sometimes fell asleep on the hall floor by his bedroom door. She followed him to the bathroom, waiting by the door until he emerged. He often left her a note telling her he was going to be in the bathroom, which may have helped a little. It was noticeably difficult for Mary to let David return to Colorado.

During most of this time Mary was interested in keeping in touch with family and this was very important to her. She loved my mother and we talked with her almost every day. We talked often with David and Sue when they weren't visiting. These calls were a lifesaver at times. What helped a lot during this three-month period was that Jeff was around a good bit, David visited for all of April, and Sue visited for over a week during June. Having one of them with Mary during the day allowed me to continue working, while at the same time looking into various options for an unknown future.

Regardless, she seemed to have increased trouble discerning reality versus what might have been her dreams versus what she might be imagining while she was awake versus the muddled thoughts of Alzheimer's. Added to this was the variability of which identity or personality she was at the time.

Before the illness, Mary's reactions to conversations or various situations seemed to be related mostly, if not totally, to general cognition and memory issues. Memory and confusion were noticeably worse after the illness, and during this time I could not discuss anything remotely logical with her. Now, a lot of the same scenarios were occurring but with a whole new dimension of delusions and other irrational "thoughts" added in.

One time we entered the house, Cody ran up to us. Mary asked, "Who's that?"

I answered, "That's Cody."

"Whose dog is it?"

"It's our dog."

"We don't have a dog."

At times like this, it was better to let the conversation die a natural death. In this particular situation, I couldn't tell if she had completely forgotten we had a dog for the moment, or if she was in one of her other identities who didn't realize we had a dog. Since she otherwise seemed coherent at the time, I don't think it was entirely related to poor memory.

She often didn't want me to take Cody outside, even at times he made it obvious he needed to go out.

Much of the time, she didn't want me to clean the house. The one task she was usually happy for me to do was prepare her food.

Before the acute illness, Mary was always sweet, she appreciated what I did, and we never argued. After the illness started to take root, her increased forgetfulness plus the psychiatric problems started to affect our relationship in numerous ways.

We talked a lot during this time. However, she constantly reversed her decisions or actions from one minute to the next because she didn't remember what she said or the details of our conversations. As a result, she would accuse me of assuming something or pushing an idea on her or not making sense.

She often wanted to know what was for lunch or dinner *after* she finished a meal. She didn't remember she had recently eaten, and she became mad at me for not feeding her.

There were occasions I asked her several times, "Would you like anything to eat or drink?"

To which she replied, "No," or even "No, thank you."

I told her, "I'm going to fix something for me. Would you like to eat something with me?"

"No."

A short time later while I was eating, she lectured me, "It's not nice to eat in front of others and not offer them anything." Her forgetfulness made me look like the bad guy many times in numerous circumstances.

I did learn from this that, though she said she didn't want anything to eat, it was better to go ahead and make something for her when I prepared something for me. She always ate it. This lesson, added to what I had learned previously about not putting her meal in front of her until I was ready to eat, made our eating times much more enjoyable.

Memory issues similar to what Mary experienced are expected with Alzheimer's but usually happen more gradually than the big sudden changes Mary developed over such a short period of time. Her biggest change during this time was her inability to discern reality. It was difficult for either of us to know if she was remembering details incorrectly or imagining something unreal, but to her, even imagined situations seemed real.

She started making more and more statements showing confusion and disorientation, often insisting argumentatively that she was correct. One time Mary asserted Sue was her older sister who used to take her for rides as they were growing up—Sue is ten years younger. She said things like "Is it okay if I sleep here tonight?" or "Of all of our sons…" (we have two), or "I've only met your family over the phone, never in person." Some of these instances may have purely been memory issues, but the imaginary thoughts increased over time. I often couldn't tell the difference, and it was all real to her regardless.

She wandered around the house aimlessly more often, picking up lots of items and shifting them around, sometimes on the same desk or table, sometimes moving them from room to room. If she moved the item, she didn't remember. If I moved it, she didn't believe me and thought someone else had done it. Several times she said, "Someone is coming into the house and moving things around to drive me crazy." She called these happenings "crazy makers" during this post-illness time. She had moved objects around and forgotten she had moved them before the illness, but now there was a new twist—someone was coming in to intentionally mess with her mind.

She also started hovering around me all the time and didn't want to be left alone. Her constant chatter meant I had little free time to accomplish anything, whether for my job or around the house. She didn't want me to do any work, but argued I wasn't doing what I should and, as a result, was hurting our family and God. But she could never tell me what she thought I should be doing. Consequently, whatever I did was almost always wrong. She often said something nonsensical or she made illogical analogies, and it was my fault for not understanding her point. It was obvious she needed constant supervision with someone around.

The time arrived where I couldn't have any real conversation with her. She rarely believed what I told her and quite often grew confrontational, which was in such total contrast to her previous nature. As hard as I tried not to become upset, my repeated failed attempts to redirect her reverberating thoughts or to convince her of something triggered frustration, and I sometimes responded with irritation in my voice—regardless of the fact I knew this would undoubtedly make it worse. But I definitely became better at handling this over time, once it finally sank in she really had no control over almost anything she was doing or saying and was convinced she was right and I was wrong.

Mary occasionally experienced what seemed to be true hallucinations. Several times, always when I was settled in the bathroom, she yelled, "Hurry, come quick. There are several children running around in the kitchen."

Each time I rushed to get to the kitchen and asked, "Where are they?"

Not to my surprise, she'd say, "They were here, but they've gone now."

There was at least one other time she said she physically saw someone she didn't know, not a child, in the house. I checked it all out thoroughly to be sure, but no one was there.

Were these hallucinations, delusions, dissociations, or some combination, mixed in with the general confusion of Alzheimer's? They all seemed intertwined, and, in all reality, it didn't make much difference as the situation at the moment needed to be dealt with as best as possible.

It was tough to attend to both her physical and psychiatric issues at the same time. It was equally difficult to know which to try to "fix" first, so I had to attack both at the same time. Everything was happening quickly, and all of it was happening simultaneously.

During this whole time, she continued to complain about her physical problems with ongoing intestinal pain and headaches, and I continued to take her to various doctors. I was a little more focused on her physical problems than her psychiatric ones, at least initially, since these were her consistent complaints, and I believed diminishing any of these would have been a big step forward. Her physical complaints of pain seemed more tangible and so seemed potentially more easily treatable. Yet, it was difficult, with a verbal fight ensuing at times, to convince her to follow what the doctors said, much less visit them.

She was agreeable to continue being treated by the Georgetown neurology group where she participated in the clinical study two years earlier. They had been monitoring her condition the closest and had prescribed her current Alzheimer's medication following the neurological symptoms related to her disease as opposed to physical or psychiatric problems, which hadn't surfaced until now.

A major complication was that their clinic was over an hour away. I believe we returned for one visit, but Mary didn't travel well at this time and subsequent follow-up had to be conducted by phone or email which was difficult and ultimately didn't work out.

The clinic prescribed a couple of psychiatric medications for her new symptoms but Mary often refused to take them. In retrospect, when giving her these medications to take, I shouldn't have associated them with her problems. It would have been better to tell her they were vitamins and add them to what she normally took.

Medications were changed and dosages were adjusted, but nothing seemed to help much. These medications often take weeks to work and I wanted to give them a chance, but I now feel

I should have pushed harder for more intense psychiatric help at the time, even though it caused problems between us, with Mary becoming belligerent and aggressive when I even broached the subject. I was especially careful not to use the term "psychiatrist," knowing this would inflame the conversation.

I contacted several local psychiatrists but by the time I was able to make a firm appointment Mary's mental health had deteriorated to the point where it was time for something more drastic. In retrospect, I should have made an appointment for me, or at least for both of us instead of just for her, and asked her to go with me to help me with "my problems," since she thought many of our arguments and misunderstandings were due to my "not being right."

It was difficult—no, impossible—to try to logically think through what was happening while at the same time wanting to make the present better for both of us and hoping somehow these strange experiences would be transient or treatable. Mary's overall condition kept getting worse and I knew a different approach was needed…I just didn't know what. In the heat and fray of the conflicts and never-ending new developments, just making it from one day to the next seemed like a success.

I felt as though I was losing her quickly, but I was hopeful some of these problems had been initiated, or at least exacerbated, by her "transient" acute illness, and thus they would subside once the new medications hopefully became effective.

Admittedly, with everything happening at once—constant problems, complaints and continual irrational behaviors, it was hard to think and know how to prioritize everything. Yet, whatever the underlying cause of the problem at hand, everything—and *everyone* (depending on which Mary I was dealing with) needed to be handled. It was frustrating and exhausting.

I recall thinking, with the whole situation as bad as it was, *how could it possibly become worse?* I truly regret asking that question.

Chapter 11

Downhill Spiral

During this three-month "crazy period" there were no real safety issues around the house. Mary no longer did any cleaning or cooking, nor did she try. She never let the dog out or took him for a walk. She often wandered aimlessly around the house but never went outside on her own. Certainly, additional safety measures would have been needed if she performed any of these tasks, but she was never left alone.

But that was at home. Taking her places was a different story.

One time the gastroenterologist wanted her to have an abdominal scan, so Mary and I discussed it and agreed she would get one. When I mentioned we had an appointment the next day she angrily said, "You're making all these decisions for me. You never ask me what I want or if I agree. I'm not going." I had to reschedule the appointment three times.

When I did convince her to go to a doctor's appointment, it was never a good experience. All the way to the office, she berated and accused me. "You're kidnapping me, and the police are going to get you and put you in jail. You're going to get into big trouble." Thankfully, she usually cooperated with the doctors.

Sometimes I tried to respond logically, sometimes I argued, sometimes I agreed, sometimes I tried to put it off so we could talk about it later (or never), sometimes I tried to ignore it. It didn't make any difference. Getting her to travel, especially if it involved a medical appointment, was a constant battle—before, during, and after the trip.

And then came the devastating first time she tried to jump out of the car. The shock and disbelief are still vividly engrained in my mind. I was taking Mary to a doctor's appointment, driving down a major road about fifty miles an hour. She told me, "You're going the wrong way."

"We've gone there before. We'll be there in a few minutes."

"You need to turn around...*now*!" she yelled.

"This is the way to your doctor. We'll be there soon. Then you'll see," I said a little more forcefully, trying to be reassuring.

She sat forward in her seat, turned towards me, and started screaming, "You have to turn around because you don't know what you're doing. You are going the wrong way. Turn around!"

I replied as calmly as I could, "We are going the right way. We'll be there in just a few minutes. Everything will be okay as soon as we get there."

Suddenly, she unbuckled her seatbelt, opened the passenger door and tried to leap out of the moving car. I jammed on the brakes and grabbed her just in time, stopping her from jumping out. I could see the road through the open door and hear the whooshing of the pavement rushing by. I tried to breathe and force out words, my heart pounding. "Mary...stop...settle down... it'll be okay."

I slowed the car, and Mary and I both finally calmed down enough to reach our destination. Even though the door still wasn't closed completely, I didn't want to stop all the way and take the chance she might jump out and run off.

The scariest part is that this scene happened on many such trips. Mary apparently felt like she was being kidnapped or that I didn't know what I was doing and tried to jump, but I was a little more prepared and ready to grab her arm or seat belt each time. Obviously, this caused a lot of stress for both of us. There were times I succumbed to her tirades and turned around to go the other way like she wanted just to prevent her from trying to escape a moving vehicle. This worked great...for a couple of minutes...until she started the same demands and actions all over again, saying I was yet again headed in the wrong direction. It was difficult to take her anywhere.

Within a couple of weeks after David returned to Colorado in early May, Mary agreed to return to the adult day care center. She seemed to do well while at Winterbrook, away from our house and me. They picked her up with a bus in the morning. I later got her after I left from work and brought her home. Most days after picking her up, she told me I was going the wrong way home and would argue, again sometimes trying to jump out. Often as I was taking her home, she was mad at me for "making her miss an (imaginary) appointment."

Unfortunately, I wasn't the only person to experience Mary's car jumping episodes. When Sue came to visit, the original plan was for Mary to go back to Connecticut with her sister for a week until I picked her up, like we had done for many years. However, when they were returning from an outing near home, Mary started crying and yelling at Sue to slow down and stop the car. She then unbuckled her seatbelt and started to try to jump out. Of course, this behavior totally freaked out Sue, who told me about the episode. There was no way she could consider taking Mary back to Connecticut.

I later talked with Mary, telling her, "When you tried to jump out of the car while riding with Sue this afternoon, it really scared her. We don't think it's a good idea for you to ride back to Connecticut with her."

Mary said, "That wasn't me. There was a little girl in the front seat who was upset, acted that way, and tried to jump out. I was in the back seat."

Mary always looked forward to going back with Sue, and she was very disappointed and mad at Sue for not taking her this time. Of course, it was already obvious this could not be allowed based on all of her ongoing problems.

All her life, Mary was the type of person who wanted to do a good job, help people, and please everyone. We rarely if ever had harsh words or argued before this time. She had helped several women with various problems or who were going through difficult times. She took her role in these situations seriously and never wanted to let anyone down. She was now worried more than ever before about letting people down and not doing what she was supposed to do or could do to help someone. She frequently said, "I feel I should have done (or should be doing) something for someone," and was even more consumed by these thoughts than when she had them before the illness. Nothing I said could convince her otherwise.

She was fearful of medications, both hers and mine. She often refused to take hers when I tried to give them to her because she thought they were poison. She obsessed over her medications, seeing prescription bottles with her name on them and saying, "Those aren't mine. Someone has taken my name."

She often believed she had hurt me somehow. She couldn't explain how but constantly obsessed over it, feeling guilty, crying and saying, "I'm so sorry I hurt you." It seemed the way for her to cope with these feelings was to believe my medications were being poisoned. Sometimes she thought she did it, sometimes one of her other identities, and sometimes an unknown person. At times she said it was her evil twin sister or someone else with her name. So a lot of our conversations related to my "not being right" and "not being able to make good decisions" due to being "poisoned."

The thought of the possibility of her doing something bad added to her guilt, which weighed heavily on her. No amount of discussion, reasoning, or stating, "I'm fine and not poisoned," helped. I tried to reassure her I was okay and loved her, but this sometimes made her feel even more guilty about what she might be doing because she loved me so much. She started hiding both of our medications so I didn't get hurt. I think I finally found most of them.

In hindsight, I wonder if it might have been better to play along with her more when she was thinking something irrational and couldn't be convinced otherwise. In retrospect, I probably should not have argued with her when she insisted someone was trying to poison me. Maybe I could have answered with something like, "Thank you for being concerned about me and trying to help. That's very nice of you and I really appreciate it. I know it's not you trying to poison me with my medications, so let's try to find out who it is together."

Several times, while David was visiting, Mary woke him up in the middle of the night, either sitting by his door or on his bed, holding all the medication bottles, frantically trying to get him to help her fix something that was wrong.

She needed his constant attention and always felt they needed to be doing something. While I was at work, he drove her around trying to find or figure out who was poisoning me, often ending up at a park to walk around. He had no other option than to play along and try to help her feel they were actively making progress in the efforts to find the person poisoning me or the doppelganger who was trying to replace her. If he insinuated her reality was wrong, she would insist he was going against her and thwarting her efforts to try to find who was hurting me. My son sometimes knew how to deal with his mother better than I dealt with my wife.

I felt like I was constantly questioning and doubting myself. Maybe taking the blame or burden off her and putting it on someone else who didn't exist would have calmed the situation or decreased her guilt, at least temporarily. But who knows, as feeding her delusions could have made them worse. And laying the blame on one of her other identities may not have worked, since they were all part of her. When you're in the middle of a crisis it's difficult to think clearly about all the options and potential ramifications.

Mary's belief that I was the one with the cognitive problems, whether due to poisoning or otherwise, led to a number of conflicts and confrontations as she hardly ever believed me. Eventually she told me she thought that we both had Alzheimer's to the same degree. I had a sudden moment of clarity and seized the opportunity to ask, "Since we both have a problem, how about if we go see a doctor together so we can both get some help?"

I had tried such an approach several times before, but it didn't work at the time because she was convinced nothing was wrong with her.

This time, Mary simply replied, "That sounds like it might work."

With relief, I renewed my search for a local psychiatrist who would see both of us since we both so desperately needed help now.

All of this had taken a huge toll on me, physically and mentally. I was becoming more tense and irritable due to getting less sleep, Mary constantly talking and being right next to me, her not really listening to or understanding anything I told her (whether from a logical standpoint or not), and her needing me to constantly quell her relentless fears and obsessions.

I was always tired, and I started having headaches and tightness in my chest, shaking at times—none of which I had experienced before. I was becoming mentally drained with all the problems, as well as always feeling on edge, not knowing what was going to happen next. Added to these was the endless worry about our future.

Taking a deep breath and pausing before responding, or reacting, helped some. Of course, it was good to continually remind myself this was the disease, or more likely some combination of diseases, causing all these problems and not Mary, but in the throes of a crisis, such facts don't always come to mind. I hate to admit it, but what worked best during the most difficult times was for me to force myself to essentially become "brain dead"—oblivious to whatever was happening but responding as necessary. I tried to resolve internally that nothing I said or did at the time would help, and thus I would let nothing upset me. This didn't work totally, but it did help some.

Of course, all of this made me less able to concentrate at work and generally unable to do work at home. I also felt guilty about not physically being at work as much as I probably should have been. I was worn down and, I think understandably, became utterly despondent.

What adversely affected me the most was Mary's opinion of me. It was immensely stressful on me emotionally that she was so unhappy with me. She said, "You're trying to monopolize and manipulate me and everyone else for your own gain." She wanted to be able to do what she wanted to do—period.

Or she said, "You're not the caring, loving man you used to be because of the way you're not taking care of me."

She continually flip-flopped between feeling guilty and believing everything was my fault. I never knew what to expect from one minute to the next.

I was constantly stuck in a dilemma between trying to convince her something needed to be done and "making" her do it—for example, making her go to the doctor or have a procedure performed versus giving in to her wishes and not going so she was happier and easier to live with. This was a constant internal struggle for me, but I tried to keep looking at the big picture.

Mary felt I had changed a lot and was ruining our marriage by trying to help her, which she didn't see as help. She virtually never perceived anything correctly anymore; in her eyes I was always the bad guy trying to cause trouble. Because of this, she started having second thoughts about our marriage, since *I* was "changing" so much and not being a good husband or Godly person. Once she actually said, "You try to ramrod people into a box and get them to do things they don't want to do." She thought it was because I was scared. For the record, I was scared—very scared.

The post-illness three months were a horrible stage in our journey. In retrospect, I would have given almost anything for Mary to have had a normal gradual progression of Alzheimer's like she was having before the illness. By the end of these three months, both of us were worn down physically and emotionally. Mary needed more help than she would allow me to obtain for her, and it was a period neither of us should—or could—endure much longer.

I knew she had no control over what she was doing. It was a mixture—a double-whammy—of having both Alzheimer's and her various psychiatric problems at the same time.

Juggling all of this was enormously difficult. I felt like I was constantly teetering on a tightrope with the slightest new problem throwing everything off balance, unsure if there would be a net below or not. And what made it all even worse was that I knew I was carrying Mary on my shoulders while walking across the rope.

Something had to change.

Chapter 12

Breaking Point

Believe it or not, things continued to worsen over time and the storm of problems escalated into a hurricane. Neither Mary nor I were happy, and I knew we were quickly reaching a breaking point—and we might not survive our current state of affairs much longer.

Some days she reverted back and forth a few times from the sweet little girl to the current Mary, who lectured me about turning into a grumpy old man or warned me I was going to hell for not being nice to people.

Several times she told me, "You need to be nicer, gentler, kinder. Do you remember our marriage vows?"

Or, "I don't want you to go to hell for the way you're not offering me food" or "the way you're forcing me to do something I don't want to do" or "for being so mean to me"…the list of complaints became long and exhausting.

I hate to admit it, but during this period I much preferred the little girl identity to her being my actual wife, who was the more combative, confrontational, irrational personality. Plus, she was much happier in the little girl state and seemed to feel secure with me taking care of her and making sure she was safe.

Increasingly, whenever I mentioned anything she didn't want to discuss or even consider, she became upset and started accusing me of trying to blackmail her. One time her stomach was hurting and she asked me, "What can I do to help it, and who can help me?"

I told her, "The doctors know best, and I'm giving you the medicines they prescribed. In order to help you more, the doctor also wants you to have a scan to determine what might be causing your problems."

At that, she became annoyed and accused me. "You're just trying to blackmail me to have the scan done."

One big overriding difficulty was the fact that she usually didn't think there was anything wrong with her or anything she could change to make our relationship better—she truly believed that I was the one with all of the problems, and the primary person who was cognitively impaired. She was usually adamant that she was the one who was correct. There was no way to reason with her regarding what needed to be done, and it only led to a conflict if I tried.

Still, I couldn't just give up on caring for her. Just when I would start to become really aggravated or ready to give up entirely, she would soften and tell me she loved me and was concerned about me. She could even be pleasant as she was arguing with me. It was a real dichotomy at times. Just like *Dr. Jekyll and Mr. Hyde* in the story by Robert Louis Stevenson, I hardly ever knew which Mary to expect.

She often said she loved me, seemingly wanting what was best for us—but I knew she couldn't grasp the truth of what that entailed—and apparently neither could I.

One day, without any prompting from me, Mary stated, "I don't want to go back to the day care center, and I'm not going to let you blackmail me to do so."

I agreed, seeing a window of opportunity open just a crack. "Okay, you don't have to go back there, so let's talk about other possibilities."

"Such as?"

"How about a different day care facility?

"No."

"How about if we have someone come to the house who will be company for you and you can do fun activities with?"

"No, I've already told you I don't want someone coming to the house. I don't want or need any of these. I don't need anyone and can stay by myself." Again, "You're just trying to blackmail me to do what you want."

Clearly, the window had slammed shut once again and I felt trapped, with no air. I realized finding a workable solution was going to be close to impossible under these circumstances. My wife refused to go back to the day care center or have in-home care, convinced each time I brought either up that I was blackmailing her.

Added to everything else, my wife's personal hygiene started to suffer further than it ever had before; now she would refuse to take a bath or shower. She also didn't want to or feel the need to brush her teeth, much less floss. She needed help with these but wouldn't let me help, especially if she was in her "nice little girl" state. Often I just succumbed to her wishes, realizing for the umpteenth time that some battles weren't worth fighting.

Underneath it all, I believe Mary somehow realized she needed help and seemed to want it, but fear and irrationality gripped her. I know how this whole situation was affecting me and my thought process, so I could only imagine what must have been going on within her.

Since she refused all of my ideas and I couldn't leave her alone, I started becoming obsessed with finding a workable solution. I knew now I would have to go around Mary instead of through her.

Mary had generally escalated to becoming negative on everything and everyone—Jeff, David, Sue, and me. Almost everyone except my mother for some inexplicable reason.

She became increasingly dissatisfied with me specifically. One day she said, "I don't think I can continue living with you under these conditions unless you change."

This statement came as a shock, and all I could say was, "I'm sorry you feel that way." I think I finally had to admit defeat on winning any such confrontations. Since I wasn't doing any of the things she imagined, there wasn't really anything I could change to make things better that wouldn't be detrimental to her.

Exhausted, I finally surrendered to the fact that I needed to get over feeling sorry for myself and hang onto the fact that these accusations were Mary's issues and her reality, which didn't make them true.

Every day I tried to wake up and give myself a pep talk. I also realized I needed to start praying…harder and more often. I wished I had studied meditation as a means of mental escape. The "brain dead" method still seemed to work the best, forcing myself to exist day to day, hour to hour, sometimes minute to minute, to keep treading water in what had become a raging sea, just trying not to drown.

I attempted to let Mary know as often as I could that I was really trying to listen to her and not just blow off her ridiculous accusations. Once I even made a suggestion. "Can you please let me know or bring to my attention times when I'm mean or nasty?" I kindly asked. "This way I'll know better what you're talking about and can correct it."

She responded, "You need to be more upbeat, kinder, and not force things on people." *Hmmm…not too helpful,* I thought, trying to soak it all in while making sure she felt she was being heard.

In fact, even though I asked those questions multiple times, seeking to change my ways, she never was able to point out any concrete examples to me. I learned that whatever I said, did or seemed to say or do that bothered her, I simply had to own it. Over and over I just admitted to her that it—whatever "it" happened to be at the time—was my fault and I would work on it.

This approach was the one tactic that usually worked to instill peace, but only on a temporary basis, and it certainly didn't solve any underlying problems.

I think one of the final triggers to bring everything to a head related to the fact we were stuck at home together for over a week after Sue left following her visit. It was just the two of us, with Mary still refusing to return to adult day care and complaining of intestinal pains.

There were several incidents during that week when I "forced" her to go to the GI doctor when at the last minute she refused, again insisting I was either blackmailing or kidnapping her.

But Monday, two days after Sue left, was the kicker, the beginning of the end.

Mary had never tried to write a letter to anyone during her Alzheimer's. Not only could she not write, much less think, coherently, but I don't think it ever entered her mind to do so. However, I noticed she had written her brother Greg's name on an envelope and placed it on the kitchen table. She had only put his first name on the envelope along with what seemed to be a partial phone number—which wasn't close to Greg's—as his address. The envelope wasn't sealed, and I think she left it on the table assuming it would get to him somehow.

Up until this point I had never looked at Mary's personal correspondence, but I felt the need under the circumstances, so I opened the envelope. The message held only a few words but they were powerful. "Greg, help me. I'm being held captive. You have to do something. Help me. Mary."

I sadly put the letter away knowing it would be a no-win situation to confront her about it, and she never brought it up. *I can let this go,* I told myself. *Let the storm blow over.*

Several years later I found another note that had been written around the same time: "Barbara—please help me. We are being held in my home by my husband, without my consent. Please call for help for me!"

And just when I thought our situation couldn't get any worse, it did.

Out of nowhere a few days later Mary said, "You've been beating me every day of my life. But I love you anyway."

My heart sank. *She thought I was beating her!*

I couldn't believe that my wife, the woman I had loved for more than thirty-five years, was now obsessed with the belief I had been hitting her and hurting her, which I never did nor would have ever done.

I tried to ignore her accusation, but then she made it again. And again on multiple occasions. I forced myself to be logical despite the deep pain inside but one day I couldn't keep my feelings in any longer; I had to defend myself. "If I've been beating you, do you have any bruises or such?" I asked her.

She said, "Yes, I do," and proceeded to show me the "bruises." She pulled up her sleeves and started pointing to every mole or blemish on her arms she had always had. "See!"

Her belief was depressing, draining, demoralizing. There was nothing I could say or do to convince her that everything she felt, thought and said was not the truth.

I felt utterly defeated, lost, hopeless. Life was slowly starting to feel more like death to me. I felt like a zombie or robot, a shell of a human being, going through the motions of my marriage, if that's what I could even call it anymore. We were in crisis mode and both of us were at a breaking point. Something—almost anything—had to change. I knew this was it. I couldn't cope anymore. I needed help.

I again contemplated whether I should quit my job, if this would even be feasible in the long term for either of us. After giving it some thought I realized this would not solve anything and would likely only escalate problems over time under the current circumstances. I wasn't so much worried about the money as I was about our spending too much time together. Even though I worked from home much of the time now, I needed work now to maintain some level of sanity.

Yet I knew something had to give because Mary couldn't be alone anymore, not even for minutes at a time. She wouldn't allow me to provide the medical or psychiatric help she needed. And continuing as is was obviously no solution.

My original long-term plan was to have Mary involved at the senior center, then adult day care, followed by in-home care, and later a residential facility when and if needed—way down the line.

I had investigated other adult day care possibilities over the past few months to make sure I knew all the options. But now there was no adult day care center that would be appropriate for Mary, or more accurately, that Mary would be appropriate for in her current state. Furthermore, she refused to go back now, believing it was all some type of blackmail scheme on my part. But there was no denying she had reached the point where she needed consistent, professional help.

My next step in the above well-thought-out and logical plan (ha!) was to have in-home care. She never liked the idea of anyone coming into the house and became upset if I even mentioned it. Based on her recent behavior, there was little doubt she would physically resist it. I could picture her escaping, literally running away from home, and I gravely feared the consequences. Plus, I'd have to listen to her rantings about how much she didn't want it. Regardless, I also came to the conclusion that one person could not offer her the interactions with other people and variety of activities she enjoyed. Even if she had accepted in-home care, I realized it wouldn't work because of all of her continued fears about the house and me.

Still, this had all progressed so fast, in a matter of less than three months, that neither she nor I had come to grips with her needing to go to some type of facility. In my mind, putting her into a residential place was supposed to be the last step at a late stage. I certainly wasn't psychologically ready for such a move. Mary was only sixty-two-years-old and physically fit; she still needed little help eating, going to the restroom, or dressing herself.

I believe we could have functioned well at home for a long time with some help during the day (or maybe adult day care if she would have gone) while I worked—if it wasn't for her psychiatric issues.

In my "spare time" I continued researching—but more fervently now—various residential facilities, both online and through printed materials and notes I collected from places I had checked into over the past couple of months. I visited a couple more when Jeff or a friend could stay with Mary. Like selective job seekers who desperately want to find exactly the right career, I became obsessed with searching for the perfect place. I narrowed it down but couldn't quite muster the courage to talk to Mary, fearing she would refuse to bend, and maybe even break down in her fragility. I couldn't do it.

And then one day she did it for me.

One evening after dinner, I was working on my computer sitting in my usual easy chair, and Mary was sitting up, leaning forward on the sofa just watching me. She was quiet and looked pensive. When I glanced up at her, she looked me in the eyes and said in a quite serious tone, "You know, Marc, you're going to have to stop beating me every day."

Having given up on convincing her otherwise, this time I decided to seize her accusation as an opportunity. "Since you think I'm beating you, and you're afraid of living here, do you think it would be better if you stayed somewhere else for a while?"

I had no idea what kind of reaction to expect since she had been so unpredictable.

She thought about it for a few seconds. I nervously waited for a response, not having any idea where this would lead. She replied, "I think that sounds like a good idea." I felt an exhilarating rush of relief…followed by a deep sense of doubt. *She's changed her mind many times before or didn't remember what she agreed to, so what if she changes her mind about this?*

I needed to move fast on this idea. From past experiences, I knew the tricky part was going to be maintaining a balance of keeping the idea in her mind and in a positive light and preventing her from thinking I was trying to ramrod something on her to the point she would resist.

The decision for which facility had to be made quickly.

It was good I had done my homework. Selecting the right place was imperative. I knew the best choice would be a larger facility with different levels of assistance where medical and psychiatric professionals would come to see her, one that had a high staff-to-resident ratio and lots of activities Mary would enjoy, and one that was fairly close to our home and my office. A lot of factors went into my decision and finally I chose Meadowside Assisted Living, largely because they also had a specialized memory care unit.

Mary became excited about going. She knew there would be activities and lots of people to be around (as opposed to being alone with her husband, who she still believed wasn't treating her right). She even said she thought that getting out of the "scary" house would be good for her. She had been concerned she was the only woman in our house, so she was especially excited about having a female roommate.

I grew enthusiastic too. I now could rest easy knowing Mary would receive the specialized help she needed at a facility where a physician, a psychiatrist, and other medical personnel would come to see her, instead of me having to "force" her to go to an appointment (and her trying to jump from the car to escape). In addition, she would receive the day-to-day care I couldn't give her with nurses and staff watching over her and attending to her needs.

Laura, the head nurse, and April, the assisted living coordinator from the facility, came to our house to assess Mary's medical and cognitive status to determine the level of care and unit in which she would fit best. Mary knew why they were there, so it was occasionally a bit uncomfortable during their visit because they asked questions that sometimes weren't easy for us to answer in front of each other. But they knew both of us realized her condition and were agreeable to her going to the facility.

After they asked us some general intake questions, Laura, a middle-aged kind woman, took Mary into the bathroom to check her physically, and during this time I filled in her pleasant counterpart April with some details on Mary's behavior. They were very friendly and efficient and had apparently performed this type of assessment together many times.

They determined that, because of her excellent physical health and ability to relate well with others (except me at times) and based on how she interacted with them during their visit, she could start out in the regular assisted living unit.

I felt peaceful for the first time in a long time hearing their conclusion. This didn't seem as dire as I had thought it would be. I had dreaded that Mary might have to enter directly into a memory care unit or possibly a psych ward the way her behavior had been escalating.

I still had my moments of fear that Mary could balk again so I was careful not to call Meadowside "assisted living," "memory care," and certainly not a "nursing home," which it wasn't. Painting it in a positive light was critical. If I didn't call it by name, I referred to it as "the place."

Even though I knew we had finally come to the best solution, I started to have bouts of sadness when I looked to the future.

Still, I realized the decision for her to stay somewhere else was a good and needed resolution for both of us. While it was distressing and difficult, Mary's moving to assisted living was going to be better for her in many ways, but it was also going to be positive for my happiness, well-being, and sanity. With both of us at home, I could see disaster, like a tornado or tsunami, looming. So, as sad as it was, this move was the best option—at least a reprieve for us—as she and I both believed it would be temporary—me thinking until she got "better" and her, I'm sure, until I changed my evil ways.

We visited the assisted living facility and took a tour. The residence was quite elegant, certainly by our standards. The building had a Victorian-style grandeur in that it almost looked like a castle, replete with octagonal turrets jetting out and coming to a point above the roof. Mary had visited several castles in Europe and loved them. I told her, "You'll be like a princess living in a castle." She liked that and smiled.

As we entered, we walked into the main room which was a spacious open area revealing a staircase angling up to the second floor with a balcony. There was a grand piano to the side, a library through double doors, and a kitchenette/bistro area adjacent to the dining room. I directed Mary's attention to a side area, saying, "Look, they even have a fireplace," knowing how special these had always been to her. She said, "That's nice," but not much else, looking around in wonderment. I could tell she was pleased.

Mary was never into fancy décor, and we never had any. At first glance upon entering, she didn't care for the formal look because the setting seemed more elegant than homey, but this feeling seemed to dissipate as we toured different areas.

We were shown her room, which housed two bedroom areas separated by a bath room with a shower. Her roommate was sleeping in her area by the window. Mary was to have the space by the door to the hallway.

We were shown around and stayed for a little while. There was a bingo game going on, which Mary had never cared for. *Oh no,* I fretted. *Please don't let her change her mind.*

But fortunately, we then saw that some residents were playing trivia with one of the staff members. Mary looked like an eager little kid wanting to join in. She loved trivia games. I could breathe again.

The plan was for her to move in within a few days after all of the paperwork was completed, along with a medical report and release with a new TB test. I didn't realize it could take several days to arrange moving into such a facility.

The last couple of days while she was still home, Mary wandered around the house, looking for her new roommate, so I asked a couple of her female friends to come to the house to be with her some. She was quite confused and continued to be negative in some respects toward me, as she was before, but was eager to have a new female roommate.

As I was driving her to Meadowside for entry on her first day, she started yelling and screaming about my driving too fast, insistent I was going the wrong way. Three times she unbuckled her seatbelt and started opening the door to jump out, with me having to restrain her. I tried to stay secure in the fact that even though she was anxious to get away from me, she was also eager to start her new venture.

She nearly jumped out of the car when I pulled up to the entrance but then just stood by the passenger door, not knowing what to do next. She didn't say anything but appeared excited and nervous at the same time.

"This is a very nice place," I commented, again being careful what I called it. "I think you'll really like it here."

She didn't say a word but did manage a small smile.

I grabbed the two suitcases we brought, and, before she had a chance to turn around, I quickly guided her through the front door to her new home. We had arrived.

Chapter 13

Assisted Living

We entered through the second set of doors into the main area. Several of the staff, along with Laura, who had done the intake interview at home, greeted Mary as we entered. It was very cheerful, warm and welcoming. It reminded me of when my family finally met Mary for the first time after talking with her on the phone, receiving her with open arms and a "so glad you're here and welcome to the family" greeting. Laura beamed and practically leapt at Mary, embracing her in a big bear hug. "Hi Mary. We're so happy to see you again. Welcome to Meadowside!"

"Thank you." Mary smiled shyly, standing somewhat awkwardly but returning all the hugs, her eyes twinkling with secretive delight.

The other employees in the area welcomed her with smiles, warm words and more hugs, and in seconds Mary's shyness faded. She started wrapping her arms around each one by one, grinning, and then beaming in the limelight like a princess at her crowning ceremony. She was in her glory and I stood back and let her shine, basking in the glow, feeling a deep-down joy. She had truly arrived at her new "home."

Laura and a caregiver took us to Mary's room, which was on the main floor. As we slowly entered, Mary was thrilled and became all excited seeing her bed, walking quickly over to it and saying, "Oh look, Marc, it's a sleigh bed. I've always wanted a bed like this since I was a little girl." The wooden head and foot posts curved on the ends like they did on sleighs pulled by horses. I knew she was still feeling like a princess and I said a little prayer that she would hold onto this idea as long as possible.

I noticed the space by the window looked different than it did on our initial tour. I walked over there on my own and saw it was all tidied up and vacant. I took Laura aside while Mary was talking with the caregiver and asked, "Where's Mary's roommate?" knowing how much she had been looking forward to having a female living companion.

"Oh, she passed away a couple of days ago," Laura said. "I'm sorry," she added, obviously noticing my concern.

Mary will be so disappointed, I worried. *Maybe even enough to want to leave.*

Laura didn't say a word, slightly tilting her head with an "it is what it is" look. Her eyes, though, shot me a look of warning not to mention anything since Mary seemed oblivious to her missing roommate, still reveling in her new princess bedroom. We didn't mention her roommate to Mary and it never came up again—a time when short-term memory loss worked to our benefit.

I was able to turn this into a positive, thinking quick on my feet for a change. Without Mary being able to hear me, I whispered, "Since the window bedroom area is now available, can Mary move to that area?"

Laura didn't hesitate. "Sure," she whispered back. "I'll have maintenance move the furniture while you finish walking around."

I led my wife over to the window. "Look Mary, you have a big window so you can see outside. You've always loved to look outside at the birds and squirrels and trees. This is nice!"

"Yes, this is very nice," Mary smiled and agreed with this unexpected and appreciated bonus.

I started to open a suitcase on the bed, but the two ladies hurriedly said they would get her moved in and settled later, after her furniture was moved to the window area.

I felt a little helpless but acquiesced. Obviously, the staff had a plan. Laura pulled me aside again to fill me in on the agenda; the staff planned to be with Mary constantly that day, show her around more, have her meet some other residents, and then get her involved with some activities. I was told I wouldn't be needed, and in fact my presence would be a distraction. Mary needed to get settled in without me.

I didn't stay around too long so she could become used to the place. Shortly after taking her belongings to her room, with the excitement of the bed and window, I prepared to leave— both physically and emotionally.

Mary was quite distracted with the newness and people paying her so much attention, so I made my goodbye brief, gave her a hug, and said, "I love you, and I'll see you tomorrow."

"Okay, bye."

That was it. She was ushered away to participate in an activity about to start. She didn't look back. She was happy to be there.

It seemed like a much longer walk back to the car, where I sat in surreal disbelief for a long time. I felt wildly mixed emotions that all summed up to a stupor. This was a moment of sad realization of a major step. Yet I felt relieved that neither she nor I would need to live any longer under such stress with her at home, where both of us were so unhappy, in an environment where she wouldn't accept the help she needed.

So *why didn't I feel good about having some relief?*

I drove home slower that evening and was relaxed, knowing I didn't have to worry about constantly being ready to quickly grab her. I pulled into the garage, turned the engine off, closed the garage door and just sat in the car for a while…the serenity continually broken by the incessant barking of Cody who heard I had arrived and wanted to be fed.

Once I went inside, I was actually glad to see Cody greet me and have some company. After feeding and taking him out, I started walking around the house, and that's when it really hit me. Mary wasn't there…and wouldn't be there for likely a long time…maybe never. I felt almost lost, not knowing what to do with my newfound "freedom" and additional time.

It felt nice to not have to give Mary my constant attention. But after living with her for thirty-seven years, I felt a little cheated. Mary really wasn't there any longer. She was only sixty-two years old and I had just turned sixty-four. This just wasn't right!

Even though I had a to-do list a mile long, I walked around the house looking for something to do with all the "extra" time I was going to have, aimlessly meandering from room to room with no real purpose. Yet I could not really do anything, much less find something to do.

Once I went upstairs to go to bed, the first thing I noticed were the vacant spaces between the stuffed animals that remained across our headboard, the ones left behind from those we took in for Mary.

Getting ready for bed that night, I never before realized how much room Mary's missing hairbrush, toothbrush and other items took up on the vanity—there were now gaping holes. All of a sudden I felt really old, and gazing in the mirror I saw that I looked even older.

It took a long time to eventually fall asleep that night, my mind racing with so many thoughts, yet unable to really focus on any of them. All I could feel was loss and loneliness.

As we were packing Mary's things to take to the facility over the previous few days, together we had discussed all she wanted to bring with her. I tried to make her realize there would be plenty of other opportunities for me to bring her things in case she forgot something. I had been forewarned by the staff to be selective, that familiar objects would undoubtedly make her feel more at home with comfortable good memories, but they could also remind her of what she was missing.

Mary acquired quite a collection of stuffed animals over the years. We brought in several of these, all of which had a special meaning to her. One of our last real vacations in better times was to the Smokey Mountains, so she had a black bear as a reminder. She had given an extra soft stuffed dog to my mother while she was recovering in the hospital. Later my mother wanted Mary to have it. Plus, of course we couldn't forget the first one bought while we were dating, "Pooh Bear," which didn't resemble the popular character at all. During one of our early trips together, Mary had Pooh Bear talking to a freeway toll attendant, much to my embarrassment. We also had a rather large stuffed turkey vulture our sons gave us as a remembrance of how we met, but I thought it best not to bring that one.

We brought in a couple of items of which she was particularly proud that she had recently made at the day care center. And, of course, there were photos of our family, primarily of our sons and us.

There were a few special pieces of art she brought to hang on her new walls. One was a framed picture of the Serenity Prayer, which had meant so much to her during her HOW days. One was a large tapestry of a Thomas Kinkade painting with a Bible verse on it. Another was a picture of an older man walking down a country path, holding hands with a little boy. She said this always made her think of my father, who she loved dearly. She used to get teary looking at it, thinking about the implications such actions have over generations. All these items made her room look and feel homier.

She also wanted to take a certain hat with her. It was a blue Greek sea captain-style cap. She usually didn't wear hats and hadn't worn this one much that I recall. But it turned out she wore it almost every day for the first couple of months at her new assisted living home. I have no idea why she had the sudden special attachment. I guess the cap was something familiar that somehow seemed to give her a new sense of identity or security when she wore it.

I bought a TV/DVD player for her new room. It was never connected for cable TV since she was rarely in her room except to sleep, plus she wasn't able to work the controls to turn it on or change channels. I brought in some of her favorite DVD animated movies like *Bolt* and *How to Train Your Dragon* that we watched together.

It was a good decision to place Mary in the assisted living part of Meadowside and not the separate floor for residents with memory problems, since the living conditions and residents were more "normal" where she would be living. With her room on the first floor, I also didn't have to worry about her becoming lost on another floor or working the elevators (which she couldn't do) to go to the dining room or some activities. Besides, I was told she would be chaperoned to scheduled events, many of which would be in the large activity room on the second floor.

They…we…had thought of everything it seemed. I tried to keep the little nagging doubts that crept in at bay.

In assisted living, there were residents with various medical problems and in different stages of mobility. Others were facing routine aging, and some residents could come and go as desired. Some residents were considered potential "flight risks," meaning they might walk out but possibly not be able to find their way back. Still others were at risk of falling if they left the facility unassisted and they too needed to be accompanied outside.

Mary had never wandered away while at home, but there was the concern she might, especially since she was in a strange setting. A bracelet resembling a watch that she couldn't take off was attached to her wrist. Of course, it was a sensor, and an alarm sounded if she came within a few feet of an open exit door that wasn't disarmed.

When Laura first put the bracelet on, I said, "That's a nice-looking watch you have on."

Mary looked down at it, smiled, and said, "Thank you," and that was the end of it. I doubt she ever made the connection; she never complained about or mentioned the bracelet.

Both Mary and I were happy with the actual residence facility "we" chose. I had high hopes this was a good place for her and that she would accept it and be happy there.

Perhaps my expectations were too high though. Accepting such a big change and adjusting to the new living conditions during the first week turned out to be difficult, especially since she didn't necessarily realize *she* had problems. The glamour and acceptance of her princess arrival on day one faded fast.

I visited her the second day, trying to keep our conversations light and pleasant. She was sitting in the common area with a number of others, but quickly got out of her chair when she saw me, almost as if she were waiting for me to arrive. We gave each other a quick hug and went to her room so we could have some privacy. "This is a very nice place isn't it?" I asked when we entered her room, as if I was seeing it for the first time.

"Yes, it's very nice. I like it."

"And they have good food and snacks here, don't they?" I did my best to keep up the positive banter.

"Yes, it's very good."

"Have you had fun doing all the activities?"

"Yes, it's all been nice, but it's time for me to go home now."

I felt my heart literally catch in my throat. I wasn't expecting this, at least so soon. I started to feel a new fear that this might not work out but forced myself to stuff it down and keep my happy mask on.

Somehow I managed to distract her, walking to the window, pointing out a random bird, squirrel, flower, tree, anything to divert her attention and change tracks.

Later we walked together to the activity room where Mary became engrossed by the music program and suddenly ignored me as if I wasn't there. As painful as it was, I took my cue and followed her lead. I gave her a little hug and said, "This looks like fun. I'll see you tomorrow." She looked back at the music presentation, and off I went, that emotional mix of relief and sadness filling my soul. It was beginning to feel familiar now.

I returned the following day. After we engaged in some small talk about what she had been doing, she repeated from the day before, "Yes, it's all very nice, but now it's time for me to go home." But this time she forcefully grabbed my arm and started pulling me out the door, making somewhat of a scene with quick, jerky movements, raising her voice, adamantly saying she needed to leave with me.

Several staff members quickly came over and redirected her away from me to distract her. Laura had observed all this, pulled me aside and nicely, but firmly, told me, "You need to leave now. And I ask that you stay away for several days. You are reminding Mary of home every time she sees you. She needs some time to adjust to her new place, become involved with our programs, meet some people, and get into a routine—without being constantly reminded of home."

I was stunned. *I was her husband, the one who had cared for her for almost forty years, now being cast aside as if I was a casual friend who was bothering her. And she seemed okay with it!* Mary contentedly went with them, never looking back. I don't think I said anything at the time except maybe an awkward and dumbfounded, "Huh?"

Laura continued, "During this time, please don't call her or let anyone else visit or call her. Mary needs this time to get used to everything. You can call me if you have any questions or want to know how it's working out, and we'll call you if there's any problem. If it seems she really needs to talk with you, we'll call you, but I don't expect that to happen." She added in a reassuring tone, "Don't worry. She's in good hands, and we'll take good care of her. This is what she needs at this point and is best for her. She'll be fine."

There wasn't much for me to say at this point except, "Okay, let's give this a try."

I know I shuffled to the doors and out of the building slowly, feeling rejected, like I had shown up at a party with friends and was told to leave. I sat for a long time in my car before driving home. I wanted this to work so much. I wanted what was best for Mary. But I certainly didn't want her to think I was abandoning her, dropping her off at some strange place and leaving her there.

I'm not a crier, although my eyes tear up and I get choked up at times. I don't ever remember crying since I faked it to get my brother in trouble with our parents when I was young to make them think he hurt me. But that night in the car I broke down and cried.

I don't know what all occurred most of the first week, but I know Mary was given special attention and was involved in a lot of activities and events. These were some of the longest few days of my life as I constantly worried about what was going on, how she was doing, and what she was thinking of me. I had to keep telling myself that if I succumbed and gave in to my fears, if I ignored the nurse's directions and visited anyway, nothing would change, Mary wouldn't get the help she desperately needed, I might end up actually bringing her back home, and both of us would return to being miserable.

Once I was allowed to return four or five days later, there wasn't any problem. Mary was happy to see me, and we walked around for a long time, going to different floors and areas. In retrospect, while those few days were extremely difficult for me, the staff were right. *What was I thinking?* They had apparently dealt with this problem before and knew what was needed. *Still I was only human*, I reminded myself.

The staff filled me in later that Mary did just fine during these few days, though she did ask about me some. She settled into their routine, participated in the activities, and enjoyed interacting with them and the residents.

After the first few weeks, my wife had settled in pretty well, only periodically talking about going home. She said she was happy overall, and she liked the people, activities, music, food, and socializing with others. Although initially reserved due to the newness of everything, Mary soon became very interactive with the caregivers. She needed them and they knew she needed special attention. She loved the staff and they seemed to truly love her.

She was able to receive the necessary caregiving and, of utmost importance, the consistent psychiatric help she needed so desperately, since a psychiatrist came to the facility to assess and treat her. This was all in a safe environment free of stress and arguments, which is all she had seemed to experience when she was living with me toward the end.

At assisted living, I knew I shouldn't have to worry as much about Mary's moods or happiness—but of course I still did, and I visited her virtually every day after the first week. I wasn't concerned about her actual safety, but worried about her perceived safety since she had been so scared at home at times. I constantly worried if she would be happy at Meadowside, whether her overall mood would improve, and whether her delusions and hallucinations could be brought under control.

For the first month or so, her reception to my visits varied widely, and I didn't know what to expect upon arriving. While her wild mood swings were more controlled, she continued to be unstable in several ways and had different reactions to my visits.

My visits and calls with her during the first couple of weeks or so were distressing for both of us, as she still sometimes wanted to leave, although it was nothing like the scene we had experienced on day three. She liked seeing me, but my being with her obviously made her anxious at times. I'm sure I reminded her of things she didn't think about when I wasn't there.

One end of the spectrum was extremely positive in which she loved being there and appreciated that I let her stay. A typical conversation went like this:

"Hi, I just got off work and came right here to see you." No matter what mood I was in I always made an effort to greet her cheerfully.

We started our talks with generalities. I learned fairly quickly not to ask, "How was your day?" because she couldn't answer this, realizing after the first few missteps that I had to ask simple yes or no questions. So I'd ask, "Did you have a good day today?"

She almost always responded with, "Yes." Only rarely would she say, "No."

When there was a more negative answer I responded with, "I'm sorry," and gave her a hug. I always gave her hugs regardless, but they needed to have a special longer and tighter feel to them if she was not in an upbeat mood.

A few times after asking if she had a good day, she started with, "No," which made me feel bad initially, but after a slight pause, she would smile, saying, "I had a great day." It was good to know she still had a sense of humor.

One time she said, "No, I had a perfect day!" This profoundly gladdened my heart. I've had some great days but can't recall a perfect day in my life.

I'd ask, "Did you have fun doing activities?" I learned not to ask exactly what she did during the day because she couldn't remember. Her general overall feeling for the day was much more important than specifics. Her response was almost always positive.

"Did you have a good dinner?" I learned to inquire only about her most recent meal, since she wouldn't remember anything else, much less what she had to eat.

"Yes, it was very good."

On the other end of the spectrum, Mary was sometimes upset when I arrived and the whole time I was there. During some of these occasions, it seemed she was scared for some reason, experiencing a remnant of previous—and still ongoing— problems. Sometimes she appeared upset with me but couldn't or wouldn't tell me why. Other times she was more non-reactive or less interactive, to the point of not responding much at all.

I came to discover this reception most often seemed to occur as a result of Mary receiving an over-medication of depressive drugs, as her doctors were trying to find the right balance of medicines and dosages to treat her various symptoms that had surfaced over the previous months.

During our visits, we usually had good times together, although my needing to leave was never a good time for either of us. Sometimes when I said I needed to leave, she said, "I want to go."

Sometimes she said, "Okay, you go," which was often said in an understanding manner like she knew this needed to happen, me leaving and her staying there. Other times it was said in a manner that led me on a guilt trip.

Mary liked all the staff (and residents with a rare exception or two), and when there were no visitors, I was told she was friendly and actively joined in the activities. Obviously, my presence reminded her of what she was missing out on, but I couldn't bring myself not to go see her every day. It would kill me if I felt she thought I dropped her off at some strange place and was abandoning her, regardless of the fact she seemed to enjoy it so much.

Her positive feelings toward the facility and staff made all the difference in the world, but psychiatric problems continued to plague her. She was still afraid at times, like she had been at home to some degree, often thinking she or someone at the residence was going to be hurt.

She continued to have some delusions and hallucinations. Three times she told me, "I saw one of the medicine technicians get killed." She had various fears and thought there were "bad people" around, and sometimes became scared and suspicious of what might be going on.

And there were times I noticed subtleties that others wouldn't perceive. Since I had been with her through all of her stages and manifestations, I could tell based on what she said or her mannerisms in the way she talked. For example, there were times early on it appeared she was in her little girl identity when she said she felt like a princess in a castle.

Of course, she didn't remember how scared and unhappy she was at home, or the fact she wanted to move to Meadowside in the first place. One time she stated, "You put me here, so you can do what you want to do," which seemed a remnant of her blackmail beliefs. While I assured her I loved her and that was definitely not the case, these accusations hurt deep down for days.

I didn't want our years of a loving and happy marriage to end on a stressed or dissatisfied note. Since she seemed to feel somewhat "thrown out," at least initially, and the in-home care step had to be skipped, I felt a tremendous amount of guilt and had a lot of trouble coping with it at the time. Many *"what if…"* scenarios kept rolling through my mind. *Was there something I could have handled differently that might have worked better?* All of these thoughts were taking a huge toll, whether at work, at home, or trying to sleep at night.

Thankfully, such episodes gradually subsided.

She had no problem being outside with me and we walked around a lot after the first couple of weeks. I brought a birdfeeder we hung outside her window, and she liked watching the cardinals and sparrows put on their show. She had never liked blue jays since they were often mean to other birds, but she even liked seeing them. I also brought in a yard flag with bright gold finches (which she loved) and put this outside her window. These were good distractions she enjoyed, and we filled the birdfeeder together every few days as we strolled around.

Sometimes we took quite long walks as she was physically fit and kept a good pace. Her walking speed gradually slowed over time and her gait changed some, but she loved the outside walks. We talked about the beauty of the flowers, clouds, sunsets, moon, or whatever was in sight. She loved animals, so I pointed out all the birds, squirrels and rabbits.

The initial period in assisted living was somewhat of a roller coaster ride with good times and bad times, but nothing like the terrifying downward spirals we had experienced while living at home. Mary was still having her fears, delusions, hallucinations, and dissociations to some extent, but they were not as severe as before.

At Meadowside she was getting consistent psychiatric oversight and enhanced medication management, plus all of the people, activities and distractions helped a lot. It was hard to admit but I'm sure the fact that Mary was no longer in the house alone with me, steeped in constant battles and frustrations, didn't hurt. At home she had lost interest in doing almost anything. Now she reveled in new activities and seemed to have a new zest for life.

There came times she didn't want me around at Meadowside, but she couldn't say why. This was tough to take because I didn't know if she was upset with me, wanted to visit with her new friends, was over-medicated while her new drug doses were being adjusted, or that this was just a manifestation of the disease at the time. It was difficult for me to deal with her being upset with me. Sometimes she seemed to like the staff better than me, or at least want to be with them more then with me, but I was okay with this if it made her happy. I tried to feel good about it because I knew it meant she liked being there. My head knew even though my heart was in pain, as if I had been the one rejected and abandoned. *Did she really even need me anymore?* I sometimes wondered dismally.

Then it came time for me to finally take her for a drive into the outside world again for a specialist's appointment. I thought this would be a good thing…we would get away together and it might be like old times. It was, but not good old times.

Chapter 14

Getting in the Groove

After close to a month at the residence, Mary's new primary care doctor wanted me to take her for GI testing, since she continued complaining of intestinal pain. The specialist's office was thirty minutes from the residence. Remembering all too vividly how Mary became so upset riding with me, I asked a friend from my Alzheimer's support group, Alan, to accompany us in case a problem arose.

Traveling to the appointment worked well, with Mary in the front seat with me, and Alan in the back seat. The visit went fine with the doctor, but Mary couldn't remain motionless for the scan to be helpful.

Returning to the residence was a different story. Shortly after leaving the doctor's office, Mary started her usual tirade. "Marc, slow down, you're driving too fast." Her voice rose an octave.

"Okay, I'll slow down." I slowed down a little so she could feel the deceleration to see if this calmed her, but I could sense where this was going and actively fought my desire to speed up to make this trip as short as possible.

She turned toward me, talking in a loud and demanding voice. "Stop, turn around, you're going the wrong way."

"This is the right way, we'll be okay." I'm not sure who I was trying to convince more, her or me, that this response would work this time.

Then, like before, she unbuckled, opened the door, and tried to jump out. I caught her and held her back forcefully, but this made her resist more fervently.

By this time, she was totally enraged, fighting me to let her go, and yelling "Help! Help me!"

She rolled down her window and started screaming at the top of her lungs, "Help, help, I'm being kidnapped!"

I couldn't drive safely with her fighting so much, so I asked Alan to drive. I stopped and put the car in park at the next traffic light, which thankfully was red. Alan exited the back seat on Mary's side to stand in the way of her being able to open her door. Then, like a Chinese fire drill back in college, I hopped out and ran around the car to switch with Alan, who then hurried to get into the driver's seat while I tried to grab Mary before she was able to escape and run off.

I had to forcibly hold her back so she didn't run away. All the time she was fighting and screaming, "Help, help me! I'm being kidnapped!"

I was able to force, okay shove, Mary into the back seat against her will; meanwhile she kept resisting the whole time, constantly begging people in cars or walking by to help her.

Once I landed her in the back seat, I hurried to get in next to her but wasn't fast enough; she still had time to open her car door. Luckily I was able to grab her around the waist before she could escape.

By now we had attracted a number of passersby who were looking at us, watching the whole scene. On his way around the car, Alan told them, "It's okay, she has problems. She'll be okay." Everyone just stood there watching. I was certainly distracted with my endeavors in the back seat, but I thought I saw a couple of people take one or two small steps forward. Some were holding their cell phones. It's all a blur, but I thought I noticed one person looking at the license plate and writing the number down and…*was he calling 911?*

I didn't have time to worry about it…Mary was now fighting me in the back seat, still trying to open the door. Finding this futile, she pushed the button and lowered the window. Putting her hands on the outside of the door to get a grip, she proceeded to climb out the window, able to get most of her chest out at one time.

This whole time she was begging to the onlookers, "Help, I'm being kidnapped! Please help."

I was finally able to pull her all the way back into the car and restrain her. Once it was safe to proceed, Alan drove away.

We eventually made it back to her residence. She had settled down some, not fighting any longer, but was still mad. Alan and I took her inside and I left shortly thereafter.

I was expecting the police to show up at my house. Based on TV shows I've seen, SWAT teams have stormed houses for less. But there was never any follow-up. I was immensely disappointed with the worthless bystanders who wouldn't get involved enough to at least call the police. Certainly the way it would have appeared to an outsider, this could very well have been a kidnapping.

Obviously, the help Mary received from the psychiatrist who came to Meadowside was needed. He saw her on a regular basis, and the staff reported her status to him, including her actions, emotions, and overall cognitive state. The medications helped over time, but, of course, it will never be known what would have happened without them.

Getting Mary settled from a psychiatric standpoint took some time. For several months after entering assisted living she persistently thought something bad had happened or was going to transpire. I would have loved for all her problems to have disappeared when she went to assisted living, but it took time for her to stabilize mentally. Though embarrassing to admit, I actually felt a little vindicated by the reassurance that I wasn't the one causing her problems at home.

Her cognitive abilities declined quite a bit over a period of a few months, whether due to disease progression, psychiatric medications, or most likely both.

Mary had her cell phone by her bed, but by the time she started living there she was incapable of using it. I set up her cell phone on speed dial where all she needed to do was open it and push "1" to call me, but she couldn't do it. It wasn't too long before she didn't know how to answer it when it rang. So sometimes I called the facility and one of the staff always put Mary on the phone.

Sometimes a caregiver called me and let Mary talk if she seemed to be missing me. Virtually all of our phone conversations were "lovey" and she often told me how much she liked it there and thanked me for letting her stay there. That really made my day at work!

After a couple of months at assisted living with Mary substantially settled in, one of the caregivers helped her call my cell phone. I was in a meeting at work and couldn't answer, so a message was left. Following is the word-for-word message:

"Hello... Hello... Hi Marc, this is Mary. I'm just calling to say hi. I'm here in Meadowside. It's a very nice place and I like it a lot. And they're very nice to me and I like them. Thank you so much, honey, for sending me to this place. And I like it a bunch. Thank you so much. And I love you. Bye."

It should be obvious how that made me feel—immensely happy. Of course, her happiness, as well as mine, rose and fell over the years, but this message was and remains a true blessing for me. I still have it saved on my phone.

Talking with her on the phone became more and more difficult over time. Nevertheless, I always tried to talk with her every evening if I couldn't be there due to a business meeting or travel.

As her new psychiatric medications were taking effect and being adjusted, there were times she was "out of it" due to over-medication. I knew from my work in the pharmaceutical field that these drugs (antipsychotics, antidepressants, anxiolytics) can all cause general depression of the central nervous system so I expected she would demonstrate "mental fogging."

My wife was much less vocal these days and I often had difficulty obtaining any real response from her. It was sometimes hard for me to know if she was too sedated or was mad at me and not wanting to talk to me. In my overall paranoia and guilt, I often assumed at least part of it was that she was unhappy with me. This was a difficult period for me, regardless of whether she was upset, over-sedated, or declining rapidly—all scenarios were bad, and the combination was worse.

Aside from the horrible disease itself, I think the most heart-wrenching part of it all was the period Mary was still "with it" enough to know she had Alzheimer's, was going downhill, and at least somewhat understood her ultimate plight. It was difficult to know what Mary realized, but she obviously comprehended enough at times to break down in tears. She could never express it well in words, but I'm sure she realized to some extent her life had changed forever and would never be like it was or what she hoped it would be in our later years.

This was certainly disheartening for me. When she cried or said some fragment of, "I don't know what's happening," all I could do was try to comfort her and try not to cry myself.

At these times, a long loving hug, often with my hand behind her head to make sure it was an "all over" hug, was all I could do. I often told her, "It's okay," but I know that didn't fool either of us.

What seemed to work best, during and after a long hug, was to reassure her, stating, "I love you very much, I'll take care of you, and I'll always be with you no matter what. We're in this together."

She usually followed with a heart-felt "Thank you."

She cried a fair amount during her first few months in assisted living, and I had my share of tear-filled times too. Some of her crying was justifiable sadness and realization of the situation, but sometimes she had "happy cries" because she saw something beautiful, like a sunset. She seemed to witness such scenes with an enhanced insightfulness, seeing them in a whole new way. I guess I had almost been viewing life in black and white lately, while Mary now perceived the world and all of the beauty in it in vibrant colors with no filters.

Sometimes it seemed the happy cries were because she knew we loved each other so much. Knowing the difference in her cries made my life better, because I had an extremely difficult time when I knew she wasn't happy. I could usually distinguish the sad versus happy cries, but sometimes asked her if it was a happy cry and she often said yes.

Bedtime was probably her most difficult time. I was told she sometimes cried at night, understandably so, likely because she was at least partially aware of what was happening to her, but this was also when her fears seemed at their highest level. For a period of time, I stayed until she was ready to go to bed and laid down with her and held on to her, which gave her some security. I often stayed until she fell asleep or at least started to feel sleepy.

Mary always liked helping others, so when I arrived to visit her, she was often talking with one of the residents, always a female, trying to console her or just be friendly. There were times I saw Mary talking with a lady in her nineties who was often weeping. Mary would lay her hand comfortingly on the lady's shoulder, or hold the woman's hands, consoling her gently saying, "It's okay." Seeing this warmed my heart and made me tear up with pride.

One evening when Jeff visited Mary, she was sitting and talking with a few other ladies and essentially sent Jeff away, nicely, so she could socialize with the other residents. This took Jeff aback at first and he felt a little rejected by his mother. When we later talked about this incident, we agreed that it should be viewed as a positive since it meant she felt she had friends there.

I thought possibly the same reasoning applied when she didn't want me around as much, but maybe that was wishful thinking. Either way, it seemed like a good step to her feeling "at home" in her surroundings.

Mary had always been a kind and loving person—with the exception of the three-month period after her mysterious acute illness, which I realize was not the Mary I knew. She needed to feel others were kind and gentle, and she didn't deal with it well if they were not. She had never handled conflict well and rarely argued.

This attitude carried over into assisted living. Especially during the first few months, anything suggestive of a problem— like a resident complaining to a staff member—made her apprehensive or sometimes scared giving her a sense of foreboding.

But overall the staff knew how to handle these incidents and calm Mary when she was frightened or worried.

Mary always enjoyed participating in various activities and crafts. In previous years, my wife's love of arts and crafts was expressed by helping children at school or church, though at times she did some crafts on her own. Ever since we married, she always liked to be active and try new things, especially after her dramatic weight loss. Even after she was diagnosed with Alzheimer's, she tried her hand at making pottery and ceramics, crocheting, drumming, and taking horse riding lessons.

Similarly, she enjoyed all the activities in assisted living. An activities coordinator ensured a variety of these were available. But it wasn't too long before she couldn't do most of them. I wasn't present for these events, but I know it had to be frustrating for her, at least at first. Her decline occurred over time, so there was a gradual decrease in her ability to do something on her own. From what I was told and occasionally observed, she was happy with someone helping her, or she sat with the others and enjoyed just being around and involved.

The staff led residents in word games like answering trivia questions, playing hangman to guess a word, or taking a long word or phrase and seeing how many words could be made with the letters. I was amazed they often found over a hundred words! Mary seemed to enjoy being part of these games but could never add to the solutions at this stage.

Some events didn't take any real mental skill. She enjoyed the times there was music, whether it was a live performance, recorded music, or a sing-along. There was virtually always some dancing with these. Mary was one of the few residents without any mobility problems at the time, and she danced with the staff or me if I was there.

Outings were coordinated where staff and a group of residents rode the bus together. Mary enjoyed these special trips, never having any problems like she had riding with me in the car. Sometimes it was purely to get out and take a ride. They went out to lunches, plays, concerts. Mary loved going to the free Friday evening summer concerts close by, and initially she and I walked there since she was so fit. As she started to walk slower, it took too long, so she rode the facility's bus with other residents, and I met her there after work.

Annually, the facility raised money for the Alzheimer's Association and participated in the Walk to End Alzheimer's on the Mall in Washington, DC. Mary joined in this event for a couple of years since she could walk so well. It was tiring, but she enjoyed being a part of this effort, whether she understood what it was for or not.

A Catholic church was located next to the assisted living community, and a small group of residents and a couple of staff attended services some Sundays. Mary went with them until she could no longer sit through the service. She was raised Catholic but had not attended a Catholic service since high school. She usually didn't remember going to the service when I saw her later in the day, but, interestingly, the staff nurse who usually took the residents said, "I was truly amazed how Mary remembered what was expected and the words to the various liturgies and songs."

I wanted to "go out" and do things with Mary, away from her living environment, to have some semblance of a more normal life together. I was still thinking about bringing her back home at some point. But I knew short "baby steps" needed to be taken first for her to become settled down and consistently under control.

The first test, after a couple of weeks of settling in, was to take her for walks outside the residence on our own, which went well. However, I was holding off on taking her in the car due to her past tirades and escape attempts.

Still I was doggedly determined, and she was settling down quite a bit, likely due to her medications. A few weeks after the disastrous "kidnapping" trip to the GI specialist, I started taking her out for short drives without getting out of the car, later going to parks to walk around, and eventually to casual restaurants. These outings always worked out well; I no longer had to worry about her trying to exit the car, and thankfully, there was never a real problem about my taking her back to her new "home." While she mentioned our home from time to time, it seemed, for the most part at least, she accepted that Meadowside was where she lived.

We went for drives to see and feed the horses where she had taken lessons, and through the "deer park." She loved going to the deer park, which was a cemetery where I had bought some "property," during a time her situation was looking particularly grim after she had entered assisted living. It was a large fenced-in area with lots of deer, geese, ducks, and occasional foxes. I never told her what it was, and she never seem to realize it, but she enjoyed going to see the animals. She often had her "happy cry" seeing the deer since she loved them so much, often saying, "They're so beautiful."

As an added bonus, the fact that Mary liked the "deer park" so much made me feel good about her liking our final resting place. I wasn't trying to be morbid by taking her there, but I do think I'll feel better about placing her (and myself) there once it's time. I'm sure most people who leave flowers at the grave of their loved ones have great distain for the deer eating the flowers they leave, but Mary would love it!

During our outings I discovered it was always best to walk at Mary's pace and not rush her. This was not always easy as her pace continued to slow and was sometimes excruciatingly tedious. She or we would be singing or humming, often repeating the same song over and over. It's a real experience to be taking short and slow steps and humming "The Addam's Family" eight-bar theme song for thirty minutes. Still, we were together, and it was nice.

There were a couple of features outside the residence Mary particularly liked. One was an octagonal gazebo with two chairs facing each other. She loved sitting there with me, and I think this offered her another chance to feel like a princess. The other was a swing.

Mary always liked to swing. In the hustle and bustle of life before her diagnosis, she loved to swing, whether on a porch swing with me or at a playground when no one was around.

She (and I) loved sitting together on the two-person hanging swing at the back of her residence, her hair blowing back as we surged forward, smiling her totally happy-in-the-moment beaming smile just like I'm sure she did when she was a girl. An occasional bee flying around our heads didn't faze her at all. It seemed she could sing and swing for hours if I was up for it. However, thirty minutes was about my max since my legs were too long for the swing, and I needed to constantly hold them up while she kept us going.

Our times on the swing were limited because it couldn't be too hot, too cool, or raining. Plus, the swing faced directly into the setting sun, which often shone directly into our eyes at the times I was with her. Regardless, we saw some glorious sunsets with all the magnificent hues of red, yellow and orange, which by now I hope I was starting to see through Mary's child-like wonder-filled eyes.

She always loved mourning doves and we were also able to see a couple of mother doves sit on their eggs up under the porch roof by the swing, with two little doves hatching each time. This was definitely a special treat for her.

Whatever we were doing, we were doing it together, and we both enjoyed it. Seeing the rabbits scampering around the building was also a delight for a long time. We could make almost anything we saw into something special.

We spent most of our time together with only the two of us, doing a lot of walking, hand-holding, hugging, and of course singing. We sang lots of different songs—some oldies, some classical, some fun kids' songs. A couple of the more common ones were "I've Been Working on the Railroad" and the popular song about "The wheels on the bus go 'round and 'round."

Our "travel song" when we were out and about in the car was the William Tell Overture (Lone Ranger theme song), for which we had our simplified version down perfect. David's musical group *Feast* had played this; we loved how they arranged it, and it stuck with us.

We also made up a lot of tunes. When I couldn't think of an appropriate song to sing at the time, I started putting some notes together and one of two things happened; sometimes my random notes reminded me of a good tune Mary knew, so I transitioned to that and she joined in. Other times she joined in my nonsensical tune and before we knew it, we had our own new original. One of the early ones we made up stuck with us and was one of our favorites to walk to and often dance to. There were no words to it, and we occasionally jazzed it up or had a counter-melody going between the two of us. It has a special meaning to us and (I hope) we will never forget how it goes.

We had a new normal for our lives and started to truly enjoy the simple things in life together. The world quit spinning around us so fast, and we could take it slow, whether walking, talking, singing, or just being together. Admittedly, I often went straight from the office to see Mary and then had more work to do after finally arriving home, so this could be somewhat stressful. Over time I expected this would be the case, so I tried to "adjust" and slow down during my time with her. My internal attitude change, where I could devote myself to her fully, made a noticeable difference in both Mary's and my enjoyment of our time together.

It's amazing how Mary taught me to enjoy life once I could "stop and smell the roses"—literally and figuratively. My focusing on her, blocking out the hustle and bustle of life, allowed me to truly enjoy the simple things usually taken for granted. One lesson learned was that "simple is good," and I tried not to hurry or complicate things like I used to do since this had only led to both of us being frustrated.

Over the first several months in assisted living, she seemed to come to the realization she needed to be there. It was a blessing once she reached the point she accepted where she was and felt Meadowside was now her home, whether or not she had an understanding of the full significance of it. This was a big step psychologically for both of us.

Something that seemed to help her overall acceptance with our limited time together was for us to do only fun things.

Still, regardless of all the activities at assisted living, her love for the staff there, and the good times we had together, even in her confused state she knew the situation was not "normal" or how it should be at this stage in our lives. After all, she was only sixty-two. Her realizing this at times was sad and distressing for both of us. One time she said, "This isn't how I envisioned our being together." I couldn't say a thing, choked by the truth of her statement.

Chapter 15

Final Trips

Before Mary became sick, we were planning to visit family later in the year. I really wanted us, as a couple, to be with our families again. With her settling down some over the past few months in the assisted living facility, I was hoping we could make a visit to all three sets of family members like we did the previous year.

I knew taking her on a trip would require a lot of planning, and yet it could turn out to be a disaster—especially if she reverted in any significant way to how she was during those three horrible months before going into assisted living. But I felt I needed to try for her and our families' sakes. Plus, to be honest, I knew this would be the last chance to take such trips, and I would feel guilty the rest of my life if I didn't try.

Her main psychiatric issues were mostly under control, though she still had some difficult times. She continued to have some fears and delusions, but much less so than previously. She wasn't having outbursts or adamant refusals, but it was obvious she was medicated and appeared sedated at times. Though she had calmed down and behaved better in assisted living, I worried, *how would she act over an extended time away? Would she be okay to travel? What if somewhere, she suddenly refused to go with me and had a temper tantrum?*

With the help and support of the residence's staff, I made the decision to take Mary on her first trip away from "home," and if it went well, to take three trips altogether to see family.

This would obviously take a lot of work. She needed help bathing, dressing and with general assistance but we talked and luckily, she seemed open to me helping her with these needs, even though caregivers were doing this now. All of her medications were prescribed, ordered, and administered through the assisted living facility. Each dose of each medication was individually blister packaged in strips provided to me, along with directions for the time each needed to be administered. A potentially significant issue was what to do if medication changes were needed while we were away. I kept in contact with the facility, but I took a printout of all her medications in case something happened.

I knew we needed to see how each trip went before deciding on the next one. Colorado was first on the agenda to see David and Arlyn in the fall. This was a great time of the year, and there were a couple of festivals where David was performing in several bands during our visit. We scheduled being there over two weekends to attend as many of his gigs as possible. Arlyn was now part of *Feast*, which was playing at both festivals.

The assisted living staff were helpful with preparing Mary for our trip. When I picked her up to head to the airport, they had her all dressed nicely with make-up on, and the hairdresser who comes to the facility had cut and colored her hair. The hair color had a reddish tinge Mary liked; the problem was that apparently not quite all the coloring was washed out, and her hair had turned a hint of purple. Of course, I told Mary how nice it looked, she smiled, the staff gave her hugs and well-wishes, and off we went. I washed her hair a couple of days later and it went back to its nice, reddish-brown color.

The first weekend was the Mountain Harvest Festival in Paonia, where David was playing on different days with several bands. He organized a funky New Orleans style parade for everyone who wanted to participate, and they were in costumes, played music, and danced from downtown to the town park where the outdoor festivities were held and bands played in a large gazebo.

Arlyn and her mother, Adrianna, presented a puppet show for the children and, okay, us adults too. Mary and I went to all their shows and had a great time checking out the festival activities and meandering around among the local produce and arts and crafts kiosks.

Due to the chilliness, we took short strolls on Grand Mesa (where she had felt like she was on top of the world) and went to a couple of higher altitude passes. She hugged a lot of Aspen trees and, again, picked up a lot of leaves. It was a good season for pears and apples that year, and we were there at the prime time for ripeness. Mary did a lot of fruit picking to cut into thin slices for drying, to be eaten over the winter months.

The second weekend we went to the Marble Fest in Marble, which was in the mountains and was quite cold for an outside festival after it became dark. Mary was all bundled up with several borrowed coats, hats, scarves, and gloves. She was shivering the whole time, but she had the time of her life listening to David and Arlyn's music. She danced to all the bands, usually with Adrianna. Mary and Adrianna had developed a special bond during Mary's extended stay the last trip, and Mary loved being with her.

I immensely enjoyed watching Mary dance with Adrianna and wanted them to have this special time together. Mary had a continual smile on her face and was totally soaking in the whole atmosphere. While the dancing was not "couples dancing" but more individual bouncing around, I wish I had danced with her more that night. But to this day, it's a vivid scene to me, in the open night air, bands on the stage, our son and daughter-in-law playing, dancing with mountains all around. I still get great joy from visualizing her and Adrianna dancing and having such a great time.

The biggest problem on the trip was with Mary's medications. Sometimes she took them okay but looked leery and questioned me. Sometimes she refused, or she might take half of them and not open her mouth again, with her lips pressed together and a "no way" look on her face. This was similar to what she had done at home, but it was especially not good at this time due to the importance for her to take them consistently to help control her fears and delusions.

Despite this her psychiatric symptoms remained under control over the visit, but she occasionally had some fears she often voiced to David. She also dissociated to the little girl several times, but this was only apparent when she and I were alone. We were able to talk through, or at least get through, such instances, and there was never any significant problem.

My most apprehensive, actually scary, time was after we flew back. I was going to take her directly to Meadowside from the airport and I had no idea how she was going to react. With her short-term memory loss, I worried that she might expect to go back to our house. I could feel my blood pressure increasing the closer we got, expecting an altercation or some kind of resistance—that Mary would at least question, if not refuse, to get out of the car.

As it turned out, there were no problems at all with the return to her residence. It was reassuring that several staff members were around as we arrived, giving her hugs, telling her how happy they were to see her, making her feel welcome, loved, and "at home."

Since the Colorado trip worked out so well, we went to Texas the next month to see my family—my mother, my brother Joe and his wife Kay, and an aunt and cousin and her family. My needing to help Mary with virtually everything didn't seem to bother her, but it was much more difficult for my mother compared to our last visit.

Mary was now totally dependent on me for anything food or bathroom-related, and communication was a bigger problem. It seemed obvious to me as they were sitting close together that Mom and Mary so much wanted to talk with each other, but for Mary the words or thoughts just weren't there. While Mom made superficial comments, she purposefully didn't want to ask or say anything that Mary couldn't follow, since she thought that would likely lead to even more awkwardness. Still, we had a great time with my family and it was worth the effort.

Waiting for the plane at the gate coming back caused a bit of apprehension. Mary was pacing, looking out the window at the planes, and several times said, "Something isn't right. We need to leave."

"It's all okay, we'll be boarding the plane soon."

"Something's definitely not right. We need to go now," she said a few minutes later, grabbing my arm and pulling me away from the gate area.

I kept trying to distract her. I tried to explain the situation to her logically (yeah, I know), which only made it worse. She wanted to leave more and more, pulling me by my arm several times.

It seemed like an eternity waiting at the gate area, periodically leaving for a short distance, and each time returning only to wait longer. I explained the situation to the gate agent, and we were allowed to board the plane first, which was a lifesaver.

Again, I felt a lot of apprehension on the return trip to Meadowside from the airport, but her going into the residence went well again. What a relief!

About a month later, our last venture was a road trip to Connecticut over a long weekend to visit Mary's family. It was now even more awkward for some of the extended family to talk or interact with her, both on their part and on Mary's. There often seemed to be some deadly silences, as it was understandably difficult for others to know what to say to her. It was a relief to everyone when I acted as an intermediary to get her involved and get some interaction going by filling in the conversation gaps—which didn't come naturally to me, but I was used to doing so by now.

Mary had not yet become fully controlled or regulated on the medications. Some of her fears were resurfacing. She was afraid to sleep upstairs with me but was okay on a sofa in the room where Sue slept and the dogs stayed. She seemed to dissociate to one of her other identities, not the sweet little girl, a fair amount over this trip. I doubt her family noticed this since a lot of what she said and did was strange to them. She had reverted to being concerned about someone trying to poison me with my medications. She told her sister, "Niece Mary wants to murder my husband." She again refused to take her medications at times with all her worries.

The worst part of this trip was driving back. She was upset with me for some reason that morning before we started home, and this continued all the way back to her residence. She didn't want to talk or cooperate. It was an eight-hour trip, so I stopped at several rest areas along the way. She needed my help by this time and couldn't go into the facility alone. The first three stops I got out of the car, walked around to her side, opened her door, gave her my hand, and said, quite pleasantly I might add, "Let's go use the restroom."

Without looking at me, she adamantly refused with, "No, I don't want to go," or "No, I don't need to go," or "No, I'm not going." I tried starting to help her out of the car once thinking she might cooperate if I physically tried to encourage her—which was definitely not a good idea. My efforts only led to her becoming more obstinate.

Two other times I pulled into rest stops, turned off the engine, and asked her if she wanted to use the restroom.

There was a resounding "No," that was now more irritated because I had the audacity to ask her again.

Of course, I couldn't leave her alone in the car, so it was a long trip for both of us, especially since I had tanked up on coffee that morning for the trip. Knowing she was upset with me, I wasn't quite as nervous this time, actually looking forward to taking her back to the residence. Once we arrived, we were both very happy this trip was over.

By the end of these visits, all of our family members could see that Mary's Alzheimer's had progressed substantially since the last time they saw her. She needed more and more help from me each of these successive trips.

I knew each time we left the residence for the road I was taking a big chance, but I felt compelled since I knew these would undoubtedly be her last such trips. I realized she likely wouldn't remember them for very long, but the families would, and that was important. These trips were stressful and draining but were worth it. Had we not traveled, I'm sure I would have had to live with guilt and regret the rest of my days.

During the previous few months I had thought about bringing my wife back home to live once her psychiatric issues came under control. I knew she wasn't at that stage yet, but I considered these trips a test. Her fears obviously continued, but it was her refusal of my help on the last trip that confirmed bringing her home was not a good idea—at least not yet. What happened over the following few months would be crucial to making this decision.

Chapter 16

A Dreaded Change

About two months after returning from our last trip, a total of less than eight months in assisted living, the head nurse, Laura, the head of assisted living, Kimberly, and the head of the memory care unit, Nancy, wanted a meeting with me. I couldn't imagine it was already time for Mary to move "up" a level in care (or down a level, depending on how you look at it) to Meadowside's special memory care unit. It would mean that Mary would be more reliant on the staff to meet her needs, that her disease was progressing, and she was becoming more "ill."

That just couldn't be the case, I told myself. She was still so young and healthy. Yet I had a deep dread in my gut, in my soul, that this was why they were calling the meeting with me.

I saw Laura shortly after entering the building. She asked me to wait in the library and told me they'd be there shortly. I'm sure it was only a few minutes, but it seemed to take forever for the three of them to finally, one by one, walk into the room. As each arrived, we exchanged friendly awkward small talk. No one wanted to say anything substantive until everyone was present, and it was unsettling. Then it came...

The meeting entourage told me they felt it was time for Mary to move to the memory care floor. While this was what I expected to hear, it was extremely hard to take. There were several times during the meeting I became choked up and couldn't talk, resulting in uncomfortable lengths of time during which they waited in respectful silence while I regained composure.

I didn't think Mary was ready for this, but more so, I knew I wasn't ready for it. I had been hoping to bring her back home to live, so this was a blow, a big step in the wrong direction.

They took turns relaying the facts, which I already mostly knew. Mary's communication skills had declined to the point where she usually couldn't carry on a reasonable conversation with other residents. While she seemed to always be pleasant, they said some of the residents in assisted living didn't understand her condition and took it as a personal affront when Mary couldn't— or in their eyes, wouldn't—answer their questions or respond appropriately. Of course, neither Mary nor the other residents felt good about these interactions, they explained. With poor communication, Mary was unable to socialize like before and was becoming more isolated.

I recalled sadly that Mary's lack of being part of a group, or worse, feeling like an outsider, was what led her to want to previously leave the senior center and adult day care. In memory care, there wouldn't be such pressure or expectations for these interactions. It was something for me to hang on to I guess.

While Mary's social skills had deteriorated, she still had more physical capabilities and motor skills than many Alzheimer's patients. She could feed herself fine—it just wasn't always in the most conventional manner. Sometimes I saw Mary use her hands instead of a fork for larger items, or a straw as a spoon, or vice versa.

One time I was with her while she ate dinner with others, and she used a knife to eat peas. One of the residents eating at her table glared intently at Mary and said, "*Well*, I've never seen anything like *that* before," in an outwardly condescending manner.

Sometimes I wonder how much Mary comprehended about these interactions. I'm sure she absorbed some of the judgmentalism and negativity. With these occurrences in mind, maybe she *would* fit in better, and thus be more at ease, with people who were less critical and more accepting of such mannerisms in the memory care unit, I told myself. *Another positive.*

Mary had also developed some incontinence starting over the period of our trips. It's not uncommon for residents in assisted living to have this problem, and this by itself wasn't a big issue, but it was another factor that limited her and required more attentive care.

Looking back, I knew she was also less able over time to participate in many of the activities requiring any real thought or skill. The staff involved her, but she needed more one-on-one help. For example, she couldn't color a picture or do any craft that required understanding of what was needed. Nevertheless, she still enjoyed being present. There would be more structured activities in memory care she would probably like better because she would be able to participate in them.

Laura, Kimberly and Nancy told me that Mary could also continue certain activities with the assisted living group, such as going on rides and outings, and she could be involved with the musical events she loved. In addition, memory care had their own music and bus outings.

The last, and probably best, reason they told me the move would be good was that the staff-to-resident ratio was higher in memory care. Mary loved interacting with the caregivers and other employees in assisted living—the problem was with the residents. On the memory care floor, she would have more staff to talk with, and people who could devote more individual attention to her.

I agreed to the change, though I didn't feel I had a choice. Their emphasis was on the fact they thought that placing Mary in memory care would make her happier for a variety of reasons. *And that was all I really wanted…right?*

Preparing for the transition had already begun with the staff having previously started taking Mary to some activities on the memory care floor to see how she fit in. They told me she enjoyed them and appeared more at ease than she had recently in the assisted living part of the facility.

Knowing this wasn't going to be such an abrupt change for Mary comforted me. *But what about Mary? Would she be scared to move?* The time came for us to show my wife her newest "home." She'd be moving "up" (to the fourth floor). Nancy was proud of her memory care unit and took Mary and me up to show us. Laura came along also.

Exiting the elevator I immediately noticed that the layout was different from the other floors of the facility, which wasn't surprising since all of the floors at Meadowside were arranged differently from one another, a design feature I thought made it look and feel more like a home than an institution.

There was a central room with windows that was a hub for staff to handle their administrative tasks. While this room was not meant to be a hang-out for residents, the door to the room was usually open, and residents could enter to talk with a staff member or sit for a while if they wanted. The floor also had its own drug room, which was adjacent to the office with the door always locked if no one was there. A circular hallway surrounded the office and pharmacy.

Nancy showed us the large community room with lots of comfortable, living room type chairs and a large screen TV, informing us that is where residents "hung out" together, watching TV after dinner in the evening before going to bed. This is where most of the activities occurred if tables weren't needed. "Do you see that small area on the other side of the room with the double doors and a window overlooking the entry to the building?" Nancy asked. "That's where you can visit and have more privacy but still be in the main area," she told us. Mary was looking around at the people sitting there, both residents and caregivers, seemingly taking note.

Next we toured the dining area, which would double as an activities room for crafts or bingo. Nancy pointed to an open kitchen area. "All meals are prepared in the main kitchen on the first floor, but this is where food is kept warm or cold and served," she explained. Mary loved the food so it was good to know she would be enjoying the same meals she had before.

Then our tour guide led us proudly to the outside patio. Tables with umbrellas and comfortable outdoor furniture adorned the area, along with birdfeeders, hanging plants, potted trees, and a few planting pots for the residents to grow tomatoes. The sides of the patio were see-through with sturdy lattice work that was high and structured so no one could scale them. "Since some of the residents on the fourth floor rarely go downstairs or outside, this is a great way to get outdoors and enjoy good weather in a secure environment," Laura said. But we had already lost Mary, who was watching the birds on a bird feeder.

The last stop on the tour was Mary's bedroom at the end of one of the halls. We were holding hands and entered together. It was a two-bedroom suite with a roomy shared area, a sink, long vanity, cabinets, and a small refrigerator. They showed us the shared bathroom and finally her private bedroom.

Laura told us that Mary could keep her sleigh bed, although the legs were going to be shortened so she wasn't so high off the floor. Mary had been taking everything in without much reaction one way or the other, but she sported a nice smile when I emphasized she was keeping her princess bed, saying, "That's nice."

The curtains were drawn open showing a bright wintery morning out the back of the building. The windows faced west so she would be able to see some glorious sunsets from her room.

Welcome home Mary, I thought, feeling relief for the first time that she was in the right place after all. My fears and apprehensions were unfounded. Mary was fine with the move and seemed to feel "at home" right away, likely more so than she did before.

In assisted living, Mary had often sat quietly by herself, especially in the later evening after I left, as most residents went to their rooms early to read, watch TV, or go to bed. I'm sure she had felt lonely and isolated sitting by herself in the foyer, or in her room by herself, before it was time for bed, which was rare.

In the evening in memory care, residents congregated in the common area to either watch TV or listen to music until it was time for them to be taken care of to go to bed, so she was never by herself except when she was in bed.

Mary's DVD player and CD player were put in her new room. She still liked listening to music while going to sleep, most often contemporary Christian groups, and we could still watch her favorite movies together.

Suite doors or bedroom doors that opened directly into a hallway were sometimes kept locked since some residents at times wandered around, opened doors where possible, and went in. There wasn't anything malicious about it, but it wasn't good for others to be able to enter someone else's room on their own. Bedroom doors were always unlocked from the inside, so Mary could always go to the common area if she got up during the night.

Shortly after Mary moved to memory care, Alice moved in and "buddied up" with her. She was about Mary's age with longer graying hair and, like Mary, was physically able to walk around and do anything she wanted. I don't know why Alice was there, but she usually talked about wanting to leave and often had something to complain about. But this didn't seem to bother Mary much. She just wanted a friend to talk to—it didn't much matter what the conversation entailed. Besides, Mary was less and less able to understand and respond appropriately. I often watched them sit in the community room, facing each other, talking and smiling. It warmed my heart that Mary had a friend to call her own.

I obtained permission to take Alice on a couple of rides with Mary and me. I didn't want to take a chance, so it was always for a scenic drive without getting out of the car. One time we went to the Seneca Creek State Park Winter Lights Festival where we slowly drove through hundreds of illuminated moving characters and displays at Christmastime.

Alice moved out after a few months, but Mary never asked about her and didn't seem to miss her after she was gone. What was happening currently was what was meaningful to Mary, apparently not remembering the past or, at least that I could tell, thinking about the future.

While it was difficult for me to accept initially, the switch to memory care worked extremely well overall, and this was no doubt better for Mary's abilities and interests at the time. She actually had more freedom in the memory care unit, and less isolation.

All of memory care was on one floor, and she had the autonomy to walk around the whole unit, plus she no longer had to wear her alarm bracelet. There was more of a community living mindset, since many residents didn't or couldn't stay in their room alone except when in bed, whereas it was common for residents in assisted living to go and be in their room alone. In memory care, it was expected that a group of residents and staff would always be together, except at night when everyone was asleep.

I was told there were times Mary got up in the middle of the night, and a staff member was always available to talk with her or, on occasion, watch a movie with her.

I sometimes visited while she was eating, observing the dining environment was better for her. No one cared if she ate with a knife, ate salad dressing or tartar sauce separately, picked up a bowl of soup and drank it, or ate with her hands. Memory care residents were unconditionally accepted at whatever level they were on, and socially appropriate niceties weren't that important here.

Residents who could were taken outside for walks, along with those in wheelchairs. The memory care unit was spacious and a nice place to be, but the getaways allowed almost everyone a chance to get out in the real world a bit.

There were live performances, music and dancing, and a variety of group activities that took less cognitive and physical ability than those in assisted living. Balloons or a big blown up ball were tossed around or there was bowling with large inflated pins. Sing-alongs were fairly common. Some played simple word games or bingo. There seemed to be some sort of exercise session most days. Almost everyone could get involved to some extent and have a good time if they allowed themselves to do so.

Sometimes the "activities" consisted of being with others and the staff, chatting and having a social time together. This involved the residents on a more personal level and didn't require any real skill or physically interactive abilities to enjoy. Mary liked being present as a part of everything, even as her abilities to participate declined.

The caregivers occasionally dressed up the residents, which was fun for everyone. Eccentricities were acceptable in memory care. It was okay to wear items of clothing that didn't match or look good in public. Mary loved wearing hats, gaudy necklaces and bracelets, and fancy clothes.

The staff enjoyed dressing her up with make-up, fixing her hair and painting her fingernails, especially if I was going to take her out. She liked it and knew what it was all about for several years. When I arrived, I always complimented her on how she looked saying things like, "Wow, Mary. You look very nice," or, "You look great!"

She always smiled and said, "Thank you," and seemed to appreciate the look and the compliment. I made sure I thanked the caregivers, and Mary usually did also.

I bought her some brightly colored dresses and brought in colorful scarves she always liked plus made sure her hair was colored on a regular basis. This all helped her feel good about herself. It was important to me that Mary maintain her dignity, personal pride, and emotional health. More importantly, she could look and feel nice, but with no pressure to do so.

One day I went in to visit in the early afternoon on a weekday. Mary and several others were sitting around a table where a staff member was making cookies from scratch. Mary couldn't help in any manner, but she was having a great time and was happy being there for the process and activity—plus, even though I couldn't stay, she later got to taste the fruits of their labor.

There was a phase when Mary was unable or unwilling to sit for any length of time. She always wanted to be up walking around or at least standing. She often followed one of the caregivers around or stood close to them. For her at this stage, this was an "activity" she felt comfortable with and enjoyed. But her wanting to usually walk or stand had its drawbacks, as she sometimes didn't stay seated during a meal or other activity that required sitting. Thankfully, she was physically stable during this period and there were few times she lost her balance.

The personal interactions with staff were most important to her. Being able to participate effectively or fully understand what was happening seemed secondary.

There was rarely a structured activity after dinner, although bingo was occasionally available. This was the time to start settling down. Most everyone gathered in the large TV room to watch game shows or old reruns along with the evening news at times. There were no real restrictions unless there was a safety concern, so a number of residents were allowed into different areas of the common facilities or to their rooms depending on their abilities.

The planned event each evening was snack time, around seven o'clock, when everyone was served juice and a snack of some sort. This was something to look forward to, and it broke up the evening at a good time. Afterwards, the caregivers started getting people ready for bed depending on their needs and schedules.

Whatever the residents did after dinner didn't affect Mary, because she and I had our own time together. We usually went to her room first for some hugs and sweet talk, then walked around a lot, whether on her floor or in the hallways on assisted living floors. If the weather was nice, we walked outside or sat on the patio balcony, and sometimes I even took her swinging. When I asked if she liked it, she still told me, "Yes, I like it. I love it."

She always sang or hummed with a happy smile while swinging. I sometimes closed my eyes and imagined the sounds of the cars and trucks going by were the sound of waves beating up against the shore, which varied depending on the traffic. We were oblivious to the wail of ambulances and fire trucks blaring past.

She enjoyed taking short walks but became less and less able to focus on and appreciate the beauty of the animals and nature she'd always loved. She always looked forward to snack time, so I made sure we were around for that.

On rare occasions when I arrived, Mary was holding a baby doll, sometimes cradling it the entire evening. There was a crib in one of the hallways with several dolls that some residents held from time to time. Mary liked this on occasion and it seemed to give her a purpose for the moment. I'd say, "I see you're holding a baby. That's nice."

She smiled and sometimes became a little teary, looking at it. At times she talked to it, saying, "You're a good girl." Or, "I love you."

I told her, "You're taking very good care of the baby, and I'm very proud of you".

This always brought a smile and a proud "Thank you."

If the weather was nice, I took her out for drives to the deer park, to a nearby lake where we wandered around, or to meet up with Jeff and his wife, Ashley. A few times we went on a picnic with both of our sons and their families.

Early on, I occasionally continued to take her out to a casual restaurant where it was okay to walk around. After a while I couldn't take her to public places where people were expected to be quiet since she sang or hummed most of the time. This meant she was happy and felt like singing, but it could be annoying to others. Of course, another complication was her eating style. And then there was also the phase when Mary was unable or unwilling to sit for any length of time. I always made sure at least Jeff was with us when we went out to eat.

Increasingly, there were times when we were looking out a window or walking or swinging when I pointed out a deer, rabbit, or something else she'd been so fond of, but there was no noticeable reaction or acknowledgment. Sometimes she said she saw them, but she wasn't noticeably looking where I was pointing. It was particularly disheartening when I took her back to where she took horse riding lessons. I couldn't get her to focus or even look at the horses. Her former "happy cries" for seeing such enjoyments became less and less frequent, but she seemed content and kept singing and smiling.

This was yet another of those sad but inevitable milestones. She seemed to continue to like taking the outings, but they were not as meaningful for her as they used to be. Of course, these observations are from my perspective, and Mary may have realized more than I perceived. Or, more likely, she was more content caught up in her own thoughts and feelings than by anything I tried to show her.

Still, our excursions were good for both of us. They broke the monotony and served as a good distraction to escape from the usual surroundings and people. Hopefully these helped Mary feel somewhat freer, or at least not as "captive," if she ever consciously felt that way. Rarely did she not seem to enjoy these times out, but as time went on, she seemed satisfied staying where she was. Over time, getting out became more difficult and not as much fun for either of us as it once was.

As time went on, the best activities for Mary (and me) were anything that involved our physical contact. This is what made her the happiest. And, of course, she liked to dance. We did that a lot in our own way. Sometimes she just sang and hummed a lot with a smile on her face, which was especially good at times she couldn't talk well. Our physical communication methods were cultivated, providing a much better—and ever developing—way to show our love for each other that worked far better than our verbal efforts.

I always attended special functions at Meadowside, such as brunches, lunches, dinners or parties for Thanksgiving, Christmas, Independence Day and other holidays. Such functions were always on a day other than the holiday so family members could attend the facility function while not tying up their schedule, thus allowing them to spend the actual day with outside family and friends.

I'll never forget one holiday in particular though…a Mother's Day brunch. Usually for special dining events, friends and family members signed up ahead of time so the staff knew how much food to prepare but also, and more importantly, could arrange seating. Mary's normal table had her eating with other residents, but for special events like this, Mary and I were often at a table by ourselves or with one other resident.

I had signed up a week or two in advance but then, apparently without really thinking about it, had in my mind that the brunch was going to be on Sunday which was, after all, Mother's Day.

I showed up Saturday evening at my usual time, always right around six o'clock. Mary and I were walking around when one of the caregivers said, "We missed you today."

I was baffled. "Why did you miss me?" I asked.

"We missed you at the Mother's Day brunch," she clarified. I had totally forgotten it was that day. I pictured the vacant place at the table next to Mary where I should have been and felt sick in the pit of my stomach.

I told my wife I was very sorry in a heartfelt way. At that stage I don't know if she knew if I was supposed to be there or not, but either way, she could sense my sincere disappointment and sadness and returned a look of anguish, almost crying, saying,

"I'm sorry, I'm sorry," as if my distress was her fault. I'm sure she didn't really understand why I was so upset with myself, but she knew I was and she felt it with me. Once my overwhelming gut feeling abated some, we were able to have a good evening together, but I really felt bad about it the rest of the night and even for several days. That was the only time I forgot such a function.

I learned an important lesson though, not only in writing special events down, but in realizing that Mary really sensed my feelings and emotions. So to keep her as happy as possible, I always tried to be upbeat and cheerful with her. Before going in to be with Mary, I would have to let go of all that had happened at work that day, how far behind I was in all aspects of my life overall, and the fact that I often had to do more work for my job when I got home. It was the norm to still need to review a document, prepare for a meeting the next day, or at a minimum go through and respond to new emails once I returned home after my visit with Mary. Added to work commitments were the responsibilities of maintaining normal living obligations and whatever else was bothering me at the moment. Totally suppressing thinking about these needs when I was with Mary was impossible, but I needed to put all the focus I could on her.

I learned I had to control my emotions and be happy, upbeat and loving, even if I felt guilty, worried or distressed. How I felt, or was perceived as feeling, was what she sensed and thus felt, and whatever feeling I left her with was what also lingered with me.

I often had to force myself to relax or unwind from the time I left work until I saw Mary and to adjust to a different mindset.

There was one event every year when certain assisted living and memory care residents were combined—Valentine's Day—with a special dinner for couples who could attend. In some cases, both people were residents in the facility. This couples' dinner was in the activity room separate from everyone else, which was adorned with decorations. A singer or guitar player sometimes provided live music, we were served several courses with wine for those who could drink it, and we could dance to the music if desired.

This dinner was certainly a special event. I appreciated it and looked forward to it, but it was a bittersweet time. Yes, it was great to have a special romantic dinner with Mary with all the lovey Valentine's implications. But this was a poignant reminder our lives were no longer what they used to be. These were the times I teared up the most.

As Mary declined, she seemed more oblivious to, or else accepted, her overall situation most of the time. But there were times she obviously realized something was wrong or was not as it should be. Too bad we couldn't get a glimpse into the future of the loving and serene, even happy, times to come.

Chapter 17

Body and Mind

Mary's biggest problem from a general health standpoint after moving to Meadowside was her weight. She had worked so hard for many years to decrease her weight and keep it down, and she had done a fantastic job. After I took over preparing meals, I tried to stick as closely as possible to her long-standing food plan. It was difficult and took extra time, but I did the best I could, and she gained very few pounds at home during the first two years of her Alzheimer's.

Moving to assisted living—where the food was great and she enjoyed the full breakfasts, lunches and dinners—took its toll. Dessert was always offered after lunch and dinner, whether ice cream, pie, cake or other sugary treats. Plus, there was a snack, usually cookies or such, at midafternoon and in the evening. These types of foods had been prohibited for Mary for the previous twelve years while on her strict food plan. The calories mounted over time and her weight gradually increased.

This created a quandary for me since my primary desire for Mary at this stage was for her to be happy, and she immensely enjoyed eating these foods. On the other hand, I knew the weight gain should not continue for several reasons. The most urgent concern was that it would affect her mobility. She often felt "unsettled" and walking helped, so an inability to be fully ambulatory would be discouraging for her. As she would undoubtedly need more help over time, being overweight would affect caregivers' abilities to handle her and take care of her needs. Importantly, I knew she would not have wanted to gain back what she had worked so long and hard to lose and maintain.

I suggested to the facility staff both in the kitchen and those serving meals and snacks that she didn't need desserts, so fruit in season was provided instead. She often left the table shortly after finishing a meal, so not having a dessert while others were still eating usually wasn't a problem. Changing what she ate didn't decrease her weight much at first, but at least this kept it from climbing higher, and over time she did lose a few pounds.

To my knowledge, her gaining weight didn't affect her emotionally, as I don't think she realized it or even thought about it. In retrospect, knowing how easily she gained weight, I wish I had enforced better control over her diet from the beginning of her stay. The problem was that she loved the food and snacks in her new environment, and early on she would have noticed she wasn't receiving the yummy treats others were eating. She would not have understood why she couldn't have them. If she had been denied she may have grown unhappy, and she needed all the happiness she could get. For once I agreed with the words her mother had always said— *"Here, have a brownie, it'll make you feel better."*

Related, she was a vegetarian, occasionally a pescatarian, when she first entered assisted living, and the facility provided this diet for her with no problem. I was told by Laura that one time at breakfast, maybe in her second month there, she saw Mary had put bacon on her plate and was eating it.

Laura went over to her and said, "Mary, I thought you were vegetarian!"

Mary simply replied, "Not anymore," and kept eating.

Being on a special diet was now obviously an abstract concept beyond her grasp. What she could see and wanted reigned supreme.

Over time, we needed to be careful of what inedible items she put in her mouth to chew on, such as bingo chips, food wrappers, banana or orange peels, watermelon rinds, flowers, necklaces, Styrofoam cups, and even her wedding ring, which she hadn't been able to take off her finger for years—or apparently not until she decided to try to eat it. She never seemed to swallow anything harmful, but this could have been a real safety issue.

I was almost always with Mary when she ate her evening snack. I always ensured she had enough juice, or especially water, to drink, usually three to four times what other residents were given in the evening. She always seemed to want all I gave her. I didn't know how much she drank during the day or at dinner, but I knew dehydration can lead to problems, especially in Alzheimer's patients.

After Mary moved into Meadowside, we changed her primary care physician to the one who came to the residence every week. This worked well since the doctor or nursing staff could take care of most of the health problems that could possibly arise.

The caregivers also took reasonably good care of her teeth, with their policy to brush morning and evening, as well as use mouthwash, but I brushed and flossed them every few days to make sure. I found out that gum disease is also associated with Alzheimer's and can lead to systemic infections and even death, so I wanted to keep this under control.

I took her to our dentist a few times once she calmed down and settled in, and these visits usually went relatively well. One time she let the dental hygienist do some cleaning, but she clenched her mouth shut as the dentist tried to examine her. X-rays were never possible. Sometimes you do the best you can and take what you can get.

At a later visit, the dentist asked Mary to stick out her tongue, which resulted in a good-humored "raspberry," to which the response was, "That's close enough." Because of her inability to cooperate as necessary, I was informed that if she needed future dental care, she should go to a specialty dental clinic where she could be sedated appropriately. A mobile dentist with all the necessary equipment for routine care periodically came to the residence to take care of dental needs, but it turned out we never needed to use this service.

A podiatrist also saw Mary every few months. Generally, no one other than the caregivers ever saw her feet, so having a professional check them for problems and take care of her toenails appropriately was important. Having foot problems could not only cause pain, but impair her ability to walk appropriately, likely increasing her chances of falling, which could lead to many other complications.

Before she developed Alzheimer's, Mary's hearing and eyesight were impaired. She had worn stronger prescription glasses since she was a child. I recall many times at home, as we watched TV together, her sitting close to the television set so she could hear better and read the captions. This was necessary, even with her glasses on and her hearing aids in that she wore at the time.

After her diagnosis, Mary's hearing and eyesight seemed to actually get *better*—to the point she didn't need hearing aids or glasses. At a Father's Day cookout at Meadowside, she started humming *Take Me Out to the Ball Game*, which impressed me because at the time she hadn't been able to sing or hum a popular song on her own. After we started walking, I could hear this song playing faintly in the background. Her hearing was now more acute than mine! Okay, I also wear hearing aids, so take it for what it's worth.

She also stopped wearing her glasses, saying she didn't need them. She seemed to be able to watch TV and see what I pointed out to her fine. Over time, it seemed she was able to see printed materials better than before, but unfortunately her desire to look at such things much less read had declined.

This all seemed truly baffling to me. I talked with professionals in neurology and audiology, as well as searching on the Internet on these topics, and no one had ever heard about hearing or eyesight improving in Alzheimer's patients. There was no way to accurately assess the magnitude of improvements or if they were even real, but by this time it didn't matter. All I can rely on is what I knew from living with her for years and what she could hear and see now compared to before. I feel sure her eyesight and hearing were better—at the least, they were not worsening. I consider these improvements as true blessings since keeping up with glasses and hearing aids (much less keeping good batteries in them) can be difficult, especially with impaired memory. Plus, someone who is already not fully comprehending what's going on around them would miss out on even more if they had poor eyesight or hearing.

Mary was sent to the emergency room in an ambulance several times due to falling. The staff arranged this whenever it was possible that she might have hit her head. Another visit to the ER resulted from a fever reaching the facility's cut-off point for what they felt they could safely handle. Meadowside was conservative and made sure residents were appropriately treated if there was a potential problem. Each time, the staff called me, and I always met Mary at the ER and took her back to the facility after all tests were performed and she was released. A couple of times early in her stay, a caregiver was sent with her and stayed until I arrived.

None of these ER visits turned out to be significant, but I guess it was good they reacted conservatively. However, being taken to the ER in an ambulance, with strange people doing all sorts of tests on her, and with her not understanding what was going on, had to be a scary experience for Mary. They had always started at least one IV, sometimes two, with one I'm sure to make sure she wasn't dehydrated. There was always an electrocardiogram, often a chest x-ray, and always a head MRI if they were told she fell and might have hit her head. Blood was always taken at least once, and she was usually catheterized to check for a urinary tract infection. All of these tests and procedures were painful, or at least stressful, and my wife didn't understand why they were being performed and she would become anxious or frightened at times.

I initially didn't provide any restrictions on how the facility handled such matters, as neither they nor I wanted anything bad to happen to her. Every time I met her at the ER, all the way driving there I worried and thought *what if…* knowing something serious could happen. Many of the procedures were already completed and she was seemingly not too scared by the time I arrived.

There were never any cuts or bumps on her head from the falls that resulted in sending her to the ER, and nothing was ever found wrong. So five to six years after moving in, I put in writing to the facility not to call an ambulance unless something was meaningfully wrong, such as their inability to get her to respond, a seizure (not just muscle twitches which she often had when she passed out), or she had an observable head injury that appeared serious. In all non-serious situations, they were to allow her time to return to normal (I suggested thirty minutes), to call me immediately, and I would be there quickly.

One day I was called after they found Mary on the floor by the door to her room. She didn't seem to have hit her head and didn't hurt anywhere, but they needed to let me know. I was called and informed about any incident or questionable matter regarding her health. That evening when I went to see her, she was overly tired and lethargic, and unsteady while walking. Her eyes were closed most of the time and she fell asleep several times.

In my usual preoccupation with her well-being, I thought the worst. *Had she hit her head and the problem was only now showing up? Was the Alzheimer's progressing more and taking a quick downturn?* Later, I learned she had gotten out of bed around five a.m. and was probably just overly tired. The next day she was exuberant and full of energy—what a relief!

From the time Mary first entered assisted living, she was seen by a psychiatrist, who was not affiliated with the facility but came there to see patients. This was arranged to help control her various problems that were the underlying cause of her needing to move there in the first place. The psychiatrist talked with and observed her and changed medications or dosages as needed.

A psychotherapist also talked with her every one to two weeks while in assisted living and these visits continued in memory care. This type of therapy was standard, and usually useful, for the types of mental problems Mary experienced, especially the multiple identities.

In the earlier times, talking with the psychotherapist may have been good for Mary, even if only to give her someone else to talk with. As time went on, I believe this became largely unproductive and likely not good for her. Psychotherapists are trained to delve into underlying thoughts or repressed memories to help someone work through their problems. With Mary, questioning along these lines became confusing and she had little, if any, concept or understanding of what was going on or how to answer deeper questions about her feelings or the distant past.

I was never in one of these therapy sessions with Mary, but I knew that over time they became upsetting to her, and there was no way she could participate in a meaningful way. After discussing with the psychiatrist the appropriateness of these sessions for Mary at this stage, he cancelled them.

My understanding from the last session is that the psychotherapist suggested Mary seemed to have adjusted well to the memory care residence, she appeared alert, her mood was generally good, and she was interested in what was going on around her. However, she had difficulty with word retrieval and being able to respond or express herself. The therapist stated that if there was an attempt to engage her for more than a few minutes she became anxious, and that asking her to talk about her feelings or attempting to interact with her in a therapeutic manner was likely experienced as threatening, and so she withdrew.

For the record, I'm not against psychotherapy, and I think it can work wonders in the right setting. It may have been good for Mary early on, but her sessions were so upsetting and confusing to her now, we all agreed stopping them was good.

She would continue to need drug oversight by the psychiatrist but was eventually taken off her medications since she was no longer having identity issues or delusions. Overall, after being off her meds for a while, Mary seemed to be more alert, interacted better with others, and was generally happier. But of course, the underlying Alzheimer's disease was continuing.

Who knows, and 20/20 hindsight is great, but if I could do it all over again, I might have asked the psychiatrist about the possibility of decreasing her doses sooner. Obviously, this would have been a delicate balance, and there would be no way to know until it was tried. While on higher doses, she was more sedated and less interactive (displaying the typical *out of it* symptoms at times), but the dissociations, delusions and hallucinations disappeared. The effects of the medications were undoubtedly better for her longer-term happiness than her constant worrying and being scared.

Mary needed the medications, and possibly initially the psychotherapy, for her numerous problems, and I greatly appreciate what these professionals did. Going into this, I knew psychiatric treatments, as with everything, can cause problems of their own, and possible adjustments or the continuation of them should be reassessed periodically as the disease progressed. Having stated that, I realize now that knowing how to make adjustments is much more difficult to assess for a person with Alzheimer's, as it's primarily by observation since the patient usually is unable to provide appropriate feedback.

Unfortunately, during the horrible three-month problem period and then even years into assisted living, Mary seemed to have been hit with a double-whammy of having both Alzheimer's and psychiatric problems at the same time. It will never be known how much of her illness was due to Alzheimer's versus something else.

During the disastrous three-month period, I was with her most of the time. While in assisted living and memory care, I visited her almost every day, so I observed many behaviors that others didn't during their occasional sessions with Mary.

While the fears, delusions, and hallucinations could and would all be attributed to Alzheimer's by many people, even professionals, I had known for a long time that something else was undoubtedly going on. Multiple identity disorder is certainly not typical. We'll never know, but it seems her acute illness and dreams brought back some repressed traumatic experience from childhood, which is often the cause for such a dissociative disorder. This might explain why Mary became so afraid of the house, especially closets.

It's quite plausible the abdominal pain she complained of so much early on might have been the result of her psychiatric problems too, which is not uncommon, especially since the pain wasn't always in the same place. Regardless, the pain was real to her.

My eyes were opened further to mental illness problems having lived through this ordeal with Mary. I have a new appreciation for what people with such problems suffer, as well as their families.

But I had also become stressed, worn down and tired from it all. It seemed that now I was the one with the problems, who needed to get help before it was too late.

Chapter 18

Sleepless Nights

Over the years, Mary's progressing problems took an ever-increasing toll on my physical health. This started with my taking on more and more responsibilities over the two-and-a-half years after her diagnosis, which kept consuming an increasing amount of time. The three months of significant psychiatric problems after her acute illness at home had really worn me down and yet I was never able to sleep much, with her waking me up so often, needing reassurance with her imaginary problems. Even before that time, I essentially trained myself not to sleep soundly—just in case.

The mental stress, physical demands, and lack of sleep kept piling up until she went to assisted living, which then presented its own challenges. I didn't consider my own health—physically or psychologically—along the way. I felt I needed to keep pushing myself. There was "never time" to exercise, but my main physical problems related to not getting enough sleep. Collateral damage was inevitable.

Once Mary was in assisted living, the actual act of going to bed was one of my worst times of the day because I didn't want to for a compilation of reasons. While it was difficult emotionally, since I had always gone to bed along with Mary, my schedule was the main culprit.

My life was a quite dull, but busy, routine. I went to see Mary every day directly from work shortly after she finished eating. I usually stayed for a good hour and a half and arrived back home around eight p.m. to then feed and take care of Cody, fix dinner and eat. After dinner, I went through the mail and paid bills, then checked and followed up on work emails and did more work at home if necessary. There were lengthy periods I worked fifty to sixty-plus hours a week, which included needing to work some on weekends. By the time I finished these necessary tasks in the evening, it still felt like I had just arrived home, yet it was almost time to force myself to try to go to bed and get as much sleep as possible.

I usually felt I needed some diversion to try to relax—or more accurately escape—before going to bed. I've always been a late-night person, or at least never an early-to-bed person, so I felt the need to watch at least some TV most nights, otherwise it seemed more like just getting home, doing what had to be done and going to bed, then starting all over with the same routine the next day, which was discouraging if not depressing.

I recorded the TV shows I liked so I didn't have to watch whatever happened to be on. If I wasn't doing serious work at the time, I often flipped back and forth between a couple of cable news channels, which presented diametrically, if not pathologically, opposite views of the news. It was sometimes fun to try to balance these to see what was really going on, but this became futile quite quickly since they never seemed to be talking about the same event, even when they were.

Consciously or subconsciously, I also had developed an aversion to going to bed because I knew it was undoubtedly going to be an anguishing time. I now had trouble falling asleep, sometimes lying in bed, tossing and turning for a couple of hours. Once I did fall asleep, I couldn't stay asleep through the night, usually awakening around four a.m. Then I typically was unable to fall back asleep. I likely averaged close to four hours of sleep a night, hardly ever more than five, for several years.

I've read several articles stating it's not good to eat within about two hours before going to bed, but I had no choice. Having experienced occasional problems with gastric reflux, this made it even worse since I couldn't allow enough time for the food to move far enough down my digestive track before laying horizontal.

I usually dreaded going to bed.

As part of my dealing with everything that was happening, I started drinking wine most nights, which I never did when Mary was still at home. This was partly out of boredom, possibly loneliness, to give me something to do while working on the computer and/or watching TV. I also thought it might help me go to sleep quicker, which I think it did, but I often awoke a couple of hours later. Regardless, I always woke up about four o'clock and couldn't go back to sleep whether I drank wine or not.

The main reason I started drinking wine, specifically red wine, was because some studies at the time showed evidence that two to three glasses each day for a male was beneficial and led to a longer life. One of my ongoing worries was dying before Mary, so I figured I needed all the help I could get. As often happens, several years later another study came out stating that drinking alcohol is not good for you overall. So this was now just something else for me to worry about.

I didn't have wine every night and it was rarely more than two glasses. I was fine without it, not missing it when I skipped an evening or traveled overnight—but back in the empty house in my normal routine, it sometimes became a necessity, something to do. I always liked red wine with a hearty flavor. I'm sure, subconsciously being cheap, part of this was because I felt I was getting more taste for my money.

With my difficulties falling asleep initially and then my inability to fall back asleep after waking up, lying in bed being tired and awake became pure agony. I tried many "tricks" to sleep, but few ever worked. I tried counting backwards from a hundred, which I had read could help to fall asleep. This did seem to help at times but had its downside. I counted down with each breath, which made me focus on, and thus think about, my breathing. It was a real downer when I reached zero, at which time I knew the rest of the night was likely a waste. I even tried counting sheep just for kicks.

The harder I tried to fall asleep, the more difficult and aggravating it became. I concentrated on my inability to sleep and forced my eyes to stay closed. I occasionally opened them, looking up and watching the faint shadows of the fan blades whirling in the dark, going round and round and round. I sometimes tried focusing on one blade and counting revolutions until my eyes hurt, which didn't take long.

I also made the mistake of sometimes opening my eyes to see what time it was, though I told myself this wasn't a good idea. I periodically looked behind me, straining my neck to see the time on the bright red LED lights of the digital clock. It seemed like an aeon, but often little time had passed since the last time I looked. Sometimes I almost imagined hearing a tick-tick-tick, reminiscent of some Edgar Allen Poe story or horror movie scene. What I likely heard was time moving on, ever so slowly. When there was a message, the phone light next to the clock seemed to flash like a light house when I was in this state.

It became almost painful to try to get comfortable. I constantly repositioned my body. Wrinkles in the sheets or twists in whatever I was wearing were like sleeping on ropes as I concentrated on them more. I can now totally understand the fairy tale of *The Princess and the Pea* by Hans Christian Andersen.

To see if changing position helped, other than tossing from side to side, I sometimes propped up in bed with a big pillow to see if this could help. Regretfully, I was then looking straight into the mirror on Mary's dresser and could see myself from an angle not normally perceived. This was not good. *Who is that old looking man lying in that bed?* I wondered, then spent more time worrying how others saw me. Propped up a little like I was, it looked like I was in a coffin. Yeah, that really helped me settle down!

What a great watch dog Cody was. Anyone walking by, any sound of a truck or animal or car door, and his loud piercing bark sounded. He didn't miss a thing. He was especially irritated by people mowing their lawns in the early mornings.

When he barked, or I thought I heard something out of the ordinary during the night, I often worked through the motions in my mind of what I would do if someone actually broke into the house and came upstairs, so this activated my internal alert system and started some adrenaline going. I often listened closely to hear any out-of-the-ordinary sounds for what seemed like an eternity. Getting an alarm system installed took some of the worry away, but it didn't include a muffle mode for Cody's bark.

There were noises galore that seemed to magnify in intensity in my sleepless state. I got really aggravated by the neighbor several houses down who started his souped-up sports car, obviously teetering with the bare minimum legal limits for a muffler, about three-forty-five most every morning for months to make an early shift or beat the traffic. I listened to the car roar by our house and away for at least half a mile. I believe I felt every rumble of his shifting gears in every nerve of my body.

My bedroom was located at the front of the house, across the street from other houses, with a busy street behind them. Dump trucks started the day early, and it was apparently a joy for their drivers to downshift gears when they came to a light to save their brakes and feel the power from their loud diesel engines.

After going to bed, my mind wouldn't quit racing, whether I was thinking about Mary, work, everything I needed to accomplish, future finances, or my lack of sleep and physical and emotional deterioration. It wasn't uncommon for me to actually come up with a good idea that I wanted to remember the next morning, and, not wanting to forget it, keep thinking about it, which led to me being even more awake. Especially in my sleepy state I knew I likely wouldn't remember it the next day. Since I couldn't quit thinking about it, I'd turn the dimmer switch for the lights over the bed on low and write it down, so I wouldn't keep trying to think about it to remember it.

Writing it down was good for getting the thought out of my head. With my obsessing and obviously important thought now on paper for posterity, I could return to my usual monotonous ordeal of trying to sleep. When reaching behind me to turn off the light, I often turned the dimmer switch the wrong way, resulting in the full force of four flood lights brightening the room right over my eyes, making me even more awake. Sometimes I was able to interpret my scribbles in the morning, sometimes not.

After such an incident, there I lay again—tired, sleepy, frustrated, wound up—waiting for the hours to pass until it was time to arise from this abyss. I never wanted to get out of bed for fear I might miss an opportunity, should it by some miracle so bless me, to fall back asleep for a bit. Regardless, it was usually still way too early to get up. It wasn't unusual for me to awaken and then doze off several times a night.

While I was trying to think about nothing, my mind took the opportunity to remember all of the times I wasn't nice to someone, had let someone down, had acted like a jerk, or had done something stupid; thankfully my memory wasn't that good.

I sometimes used my awake time to pray, even reverting to the prayer I said every night when I was very young. *Now I lay me down to sleep, I pray dear Lord my soul to keep. If I should die before I wake, I pray dear Lord my soul to take. If I should live another day, I pray dear Lord to guide my way.*

Sometimes this helped, sometimes not.

When asleep, I dreamed a lot, but my dreams often seemed very superficial, where I could often think about what was going on and control what happened at times. The problem with realizing what was transpiring in my dreams was that I woke up when the events became distressing or I seemed to reach the end of some segment of the adventure. This wasn't very restful, but it was a lot better than squirming the whole night without sleeping much at all.

If I had an early morning meeting or appointment, I couldn't go back to sleep for fear of missing it, even if I had two alarms set. This thought likely led to the resurfacing of a dream I've had several times over my adult life. In the dream I'm in college, late for a big final exam, running around campus trying to find the classroom since I never attended the class. Oh yeah, I also didn't have any clothes on. This didn't seem to bother me during the dream, but it was discouraging when I woke up and realized that no one noticed I didn't have any clothes on.

I find it amazing what can run through someone's mind when in a half-awake and half-asleep mode. I feel I now have a better understanding of what Mary must have been going through during her weeks when she was ill and in bed so much, sleeping a lot but obviously in a semi-conscious state at times that allowed her Alzheimer's brain to run wild and become afraid of so many things.

Since I mostly laid with my eyes closed so I didn't notice any light or distractions, it was very disheartening when I opened them and saw the room had become brighter with the morning sun creeping in through the blinds. In a way it was distressing since I knew it was worthless to attempt sleeping any more, but in a way, it was a relief that I didn't have to endure the bed much longer.

While still keeping my eyes closed so I wouldn't notice the dawn of a new day, I knew it was a totally lost cause when I heard the infernal trash or recycling trucks, with their squeaking brakes, compacting noise, and clanging trash cans. It was almost a liberation to know the nightly ordeal was over. I could now get up, deal with Cody, and go to work.

A night of good sleep eluded me, and some nights were akin to sleep-depravation torture. I had also read reports stating evidence that not getting enough sleep decreased a person's lifespan by so many years and was a risk factor for Alzheimer's, which added to my worries about not being around for Mary. This was obviously not a sustainable lifestyle.

My daily schedule was necessary because of going to work, then needing to see Mary on the way home since her residence was not far out of the way between work and our house. During the week, if I dragged myself out of bed early enough, I often worked at home doing actual work or taking care of something personal before going to the office. Being at home some in the morning started the day off a little more leisurely; I didn't have to rush off to work like I usually had done throughout the years, and this seemed to make my day feel shorter. It also allowed delaying taking care of Cody as long as possible, so he wouldn't be home alone and not be able to do his business, much less get fed, for more than twelve hours, which was the usual time I was away.

I almost always went into the office since the set-up was more compatible for working and I went that direction every day to see Mary regardless. Plus, it was often stressful working at home with Cody there. There were times I wore gun-range-quality ear protectors to muffle his incessant barking, which of course didn't work well for conference calls.

The only good thing about my sleep deprivation and resulting fogginess was that I could finally relate, I think, to what my wife was going through and better empathize with her. Especially during our most difficult times, my being in a clear state while Mary was in a confused one made it close to impossible for me to comprehend or fully empathize with, much less have the patience for, what was going on with her. Two to three years after Mary moved to assisted living, I experienced a glimpse of that feeling.

I had been overly tired for at least the past six months. One day at work, I had a surreal feeling. I couldn't focus my mind well, was a bit confused, and felt almost as if my body was partly detached from my mind. It lasted for a couple of hours. In my initial denial, I thought it was the prelude of a viral infection coming on. Then I started thinking about TIAs, mini-strokes, heart attacks—and went to the emergency room. Yes, I drove myself there—no lectures, please, and I don't recommend it!

After two days of cardiovascular and neurological testing, the doctors found nothing wrong. It turned out to be most likely related to four-plus years of sleep deprivation, with a lot of stress added in. The years of averaging maybe four hours of sleep had exhausted my body to the point where it just wasn't functioning properly anymore.

The second night in the hospital, I was given something to help me sleep. What a wonderful feeling to wake up the next morning after a good eight hours of sleep! I felt more rested, alert and invigorated than I had for a long time. I'm sure the staff came in to take my blood pressure or whatever several times during the night, but it didn't disturb me enough to the point I couldn't go right back to sleep.

This confused, non-focused, detached feeling was the scariest sensation I've ever had. It felt as if I was losing my mind, not from a psychiatric standpoint, but more like it was short-circuiting or fading out on me. If this was anything resembling how a person with Alzheimer's perceives themselves or their environment, I was now, more than ever before, able to "appreciate" the horrible ordeal Mary was experiencing.

This episode made me realize I needed to start taking care of myself, at least better than I had been. The combination of dealing with and taking care of Mary, working full-time, losing sleep, and constantly being stressed had finally caught up with me. I had been able to hide my problems better than Mary was able to hide hers.

After the ER visit with the sleep medication success, I visited my regular doctor, told him the situation, and started taking something on a regular basis, not every night and usually a half-dose, but it helped greatly. I still didn't sleep well when I didn't take something. It took about thirty minutes for the medication to kick in, so I started propping up and reading until the drug took effect, which likely also helped my recently-eaten food settle better. Reading worked well since it distracted me, as otherwise my mind would start wandering and thinking about all the things I needed to do, worrying about Mary, and on and on, before falling asleep.

I thought my still feeling tired and a bit out of it when I woke up was due to lack of a really good night's sleep since I refused to let myself get used to taking a full dose of the sleep medication, but then I started to realize the wine I was still drinking added to it. I started drinking less wine and imbibing less often, which helped.

When I stopped drinking nightly, I felt more alert after waking up than before, without a heavy feeling in my mind and eyes, which sometimes occurred after having only one glass. Now I always have a glass of water by my chair, and I feel better when I wake up. I wish I had taken this step years before.

While not perfect, I was in a new norm that was much better for me physically. Mentally and emotionally, I wasn't quite "there" yet.

Chapter 19

Getting Help

From the time of her diagnosis, my primary concern had been to meet Mary's needs by supporting her emotionally, physically, and financially. After all, *she* was the one with the problems, right? What I hadn't addressed much is the support *I* needed, whether I knew it or not. My belief that support for me was secondary would have been understandable, possibly even commendable had I not taken it to the extreme.

My situation was different from many others, where a caregiver takes care of a loved one at home for several long years through all the progressive stages. I would like to have cared for my wife longer at home the way she was progressing before her illness, when everything was working well overall—until her psychiatric symptoms wreaked havoc and necessitated transition to an assisted living environment.

So I didn't have it as bad as others who had to care for loved ones with Alzheimer's 24/7…right?

During Mary's time in assisted living and the initial years in memory care, I still worried a lot about what was going to happen with her both short and long term, about her happiness, about whether I could bring her home, and about our finances, which included worrying about my job. I worried about almost everything—except me.

During her first five years at the residence, except for our travels to visit family during the first year, I had taken one vacation for a few days to visit David's family in Colorado, not too long after their son, our grandson, was born. The only other times I was away were for business and to go to my mother's funeral in Texas.

My schedule was full and, seemingly out of necessity, dull. Believe me, I'm not bragging. This was not the ideal way to live life, and sleep problems lingered long term, even after the ER-trip hospital awakening. At the time, I felt the solution was needing more hours in the day. *Yeah, good luck with that,* I told myself sarcastically. I was obsessed with my schedule, feeling I had to see Mary every day.

Jeff was around a lot and saw the effects all this was having on my life, health, and overall sanity better than I did. He told me, "I think you should talk with a professional therapist to help with the stress and strain." He could envision the long-term effects on my health if I didn't change something. I was consumed by one stressor or another—Mary, work, Cody and even working on this book *for Mary*—and over-committed, trying to manage Mary's condition and happiness, which I knew deep down were largely beyond my control. There was no break in my routine. I was obsessed with everything surrounding Mary—seeing her every day for her happiness, working too hard to ensure finances were okay for her and eventually me, trying to solve the unsolvable…giving up myself in the meantime. I had put Mary's needs, or at least her needs as I viewed them, above everything and everyone.

Jeff essentially said, "Dad, if you run yourself into the ground you're not going to be around much longer, and then what kind of support are you going to be for Mom?" *The truth was often toughest to hear—and truest—when it came from one of your kids.* I listened intently, basically agreed with him, thanked him for his concern and told him I'd consider talking with someone. I thought about it some…and then went back to my routine. I didn't have the need or time for such "nonsense."

However, I did have one session early on with Mary's psychiatrist, as the spouse of someone under his care. After we talked, he suggested an antidepressant often helps in such circumstances and offered a prescription if I wanted to try it. Having worked in the pharmaceutical field, I had performed clinical studies with anti-anxiety agents and antidepressants, so I knew the symptoms and how these drugs can help. I knew spouses in similar situations who said antidepressants helped them considerably.

And yet, I decided at the time that I didn't need them and didn't take him up on his offer. I had always been a laid-back kind of guy, I had a PhD in pharmacology, likely knowing more about drugs than the average bear, and I was functioning just fine—or so I thought. I wasn't depressed, *per se*, I told myself. I was profoundly sad, but the cause was due to a specific situation, I reasoned.

Jeff's words ringing in my head, I look back now and saw the folly in all of my defenses and the extra agony I had suffered all this time just getting by on my own. Maybe I should have talked with someone earlier or tried the drugs. Maybe I didn't want to admit I was having a difficult time handling everything. After all, "real men" don't admit they're lost and ask for directions.

I was performing my ritual and didn't have time for help or support. But I had forgotten in the process how to have a life for myself. *As long as I'm taking care of Mary, making her life better, it will be worth it. Worth the sleepless nights, worth the grueling schedule, worth the pain and suffering…worth the fact that I won't have as much guilt or fear that I might have to live with if something ever happened to her the one day I didn't visit.*

I just couldn't objectively see what overall effects my dogged determination was having on my life, much less how to change it. I seemed to be stuck in a rut, like the proverbial rat running in circles on a wheel. With all the unending obligations and compulsions, I couldn't see the bigger picture.

My routine was predictable, okay repetitive, and I wasn't taking time for myself since I wanted to be a daily support to Mary. Plus, I liked being with her. She had finally arrived at the point where she was always pleasant and lovey, and we had good times together.

Numerous people, both at Mary's residence and elsewhere, told me I didn't need to go see her every day and recommended I start doing more for myself. It always sounded so logical, but there was always a gnawing feeling inside when I tried. Whether she truly *needed* me every day or not, I knew she *liked* my visits.

After nearly five years visiting Mary daily in memory care, I finally took my first vacation (besides the one I took when our grandson was born) to visit David and his family again in Colorado; there was going to be a year between the times they could come to Maryland, and now our grandson had recently turned three. A year in the life of a three-year old is a long time for both him and me! Jeff visited Mary during this time, but of course I was worried if she might miss me. I wondered if my not being with her for six days would lose some of the momentum we had built, or if she might forget me some.

Upon arriving to see her the first time after my return, I was a little apprehensive as I approached her. She was sitting next to a caregiver. I looked at her, smiled, and said, "Hi."

She looked at me with no expression for what seemed to be an eternity, probably about five seconds, then smiled and said, "I like you." We walked away and had our special time together, like usual.

Subsequent to that time away, I was sick for a week and, of course, didn't visit her. I felt sure she would be happy to see me when I was able to return for a visit and that our time together would be pretty much like always, especially with my reception after the Colorado trip. She was fine when I returned, we walked and sat together for a while, and then I took her back to sit with the other residents and told her I'd see her tomorrow. She said, "You go," in a pleasant tone and then turned to give her attention to happenings in the room. She seemed perfectly fine with my leaving. Maybe I'm reading too much into it, but it seems she had fully accepted her situation. This was good…but hard.

Did she even realize when I didn't come for a visit? Should I worry that she didn't or just be glad? Maybe it was better this way, I reassured myself. This way, everything would be "normal"— whether I was there or not. *Still…*I started wondering now if my visits even made any difference at all.

To assuage my fears, I asked two of the caregivers if it seemed that Mary ever missed me. Both said yes, and that Mary asked, "Where is he?" on two of the evenings I wasn't there. Despite myself, I felt good that she at least missed me occasionally, and it made me determined to be there for her whenever I could. She still wanted me, and I made her day better. I decided I would keep up what had become a monotonous yet grueling schedule not to miss another day with my wife without good cause.

Yet even though I was feeling better about Mary being happy, I was feeling more and more depressed and isolated. The support group I had joined after Mary's diagnosis had been good and I was still attending regularly, but I had already talked through my circumstances and issues with them many times and nothing had really changed much over the past several years.

I had grown to know the core group of five other regular attendees over the years, and these were likely the closest friends I had. A couple of them I saw almost every day when visiting Mary because they had a spouse or close friend living at Meadowside where the meeting was held. I went to a few financial planning sessions with one. Another kept attending after his significant other moved to another state to live with her daughter, and another attended for close to a year after his wife passed away. And there was my friend Alan who had helped me drive Mary the time she tried to car jump again.

But with work and time constraints these were monthly friendships, dependent on when people could attend. I didn't have any close friend as a confidant, and I certainly didn't want to burden our sons with my issues, which they had no control over.

During this time we had medical insurance coverage through my employer. A benefit was that the insurance company contracted with an outside mental health group that provided professionals to talk through mental or emotional issues and offer appropriate help as needed. I'm sure it was more cost efficient for the insurance company to try to prevent something significant from happening to one of their policy holders than to later pay for medical, hospital, or specialized treatment.

This group had called to talk with Mary several years back to help her through her struggles with Alzheimer's, but by that time I believe she was already in assisted living. She was obtaining the care she needed and was beyond the point of communicating well in such a conversation, especially with someone on the phone she didn't know. They also offered help for me back then, but I declined, stating I was fine, was dealing with everything great, and didn't have any emotional issues. I think they were primarily worried about depression, which could lead to more complicated problems, or worse. They called every year or so to see how we were doing and if we wanted to talk with one of their support counsellors.

It took five years after Mary moved into assisted living for me to break down and finally talk with them in more detail about their services.

The worry about finances had finally became overwhelming enough for me to ask for help. There was always the distressing concern there might be a financial disaster down the line. With my working full time and having a long-term care policy that paid part of the costs of Mary's care, I was doing okay financially, but still worried about the future. *What about when the long-term care policy runs out in the not-too-distant future, or I no longer have a job, or both? What if something happens to me first?* After all I was in my late sixties now, no spring chicken.

So, I agreed to give the insurance group a try, especially since I didn't have anyone else with whom to talk things through.

I started talking with a social worker, Carol, every one to two weeks. She lived in another time zone and I never met her, but she was a health professional trained to talk with people about their problems or issues, offer suggestions, and refer them to more specialized professionals if necessary. She was apparently good at her job because I found that she was easy to talk to despite myself.

It seemed non-threatening enough, I thought. There was really no reason not to tell her my true feelings. *What could it hurt?* Okay, her notes on me, my stresses, and our sessions would be in my records with this group, and the insurance company could likely have access to these if needed, but it seemed worth taking the risk if there was one. I felt I didn't have to hold back on what I told her, and she could assess my situation as an outside observer, as I had become non-objective.

I leveled with her during the sessions, telling her my stresses, primarily for uncertainties about Mary's and my future, my worries about the long-term financial ramifications of my wife's disease, about feeling guilty if I didn't go see Mary every day, and about my not wanting the dog Cody—which was my most acute stressor at the time (regretfully, she didn't offer to take him).

I told her I enjoyed being with Mary and knew it made her happy, so I didn't want *not* to go see her without a good reason. Carol eventually brought up what others had suggested to me—to think about what Mary would want for me in this situation—or what I would want Mary to do if I was the one with Alzheimer's.

After I unloaded my list, telling her everything keeping me busy and worried, Carol asked, "What do you do for fun?"

There was a long silence.

"What do you do just for yourself?"

I was at a loss and couldn't think of a good answer.

"When was the last time you've done something that didn't involve Mary in some way?"

All I could think of was, "Well, Jeff took me to a Nationals baseball game for my birthday a couple of years ago. Last year I went to Colorado for a few days to visit David and his family. That trip was great, but I felt guilty about it. I took an overnight trip to Pittsburgh a few months ago to see my brother and their daughter's family living there...but I went to see Mary on my way there one morning and on my return the next evening."

I could sense where this was going, and I was digging myself in a hole, already beginning to wonder if I really wanted to talk with this lady or not.

"What can you think of that would be fun, that you would like to do outside of what you're doing now?"

Another lengthy silence. "Gee, I'm not sure," I said, realizing how sad this must sound. "I don't have any hobbies. There isn't a friend or group to just hang out with."

I was mostly at a loss for ideas. We discussed a few possibilities, such as places to go, people to meet up with, groups to join. She told me, "I want you to do something for yourself every week. I want you to tell me next week what you did." *No one told me I would be held accountable for having fun!* Also, my routine was already wearing me out, and I wasn't able to do all I needed to do as it was. I didn't want anything extra added in.

But I knew deep down Carol was right. So my first commitment was to go to a small café, the Music Café, where there was live music on Friday and Saturday nights. David had played there before. I went there two Friday evenings over a couple of months, eating and listening to music. One time, the place was crowded, so I sat at a table with a couple and we stirred up a conversation, talking during breaks in the music.

While it would have been better to go with someone, I enjoyed this, and it was good to get out and actually "do" something I didn't normally do. I don't think I ever told Carol that at least one of the times, I went there *after* I visited Mary that evening. Regardless, she was proud of me, and we were on a roll.

Over several months, I ventured out a couple of times during the evening instead of going to see Mary. One was to spend the evening with Jeff and his family for a party, and the other was to attend a local festival that extended into the evening. The next day I asked the caregivers at Meadowside if Mary seemed to miss me, and they said she was fine without me. *Hmmm, go figure.*

A few other times, I intentionally tried to do something "extra, out of the ordinary" like meeting a previous work colleague for brunch on Saturday or attending a daytime festival, still managing to squeeze in my visits with Mary.

Going on these outside excursions, few as they were, helped in several ways. Importantly, I realized Mary wouldn't go off the deep end if I didn't go see her every day, whether it was because I had to travel for work or do something for myself. More importantly for my long-term sanity, it made me realize I really enjoyed visiting her and being with her. Not only did it make her happy, but it made me happy, and I missed seeing her.

There were times over the years when visiting her seemed to be more of an obligation. Admittedly, there were periods in her journey I wasn't necessarily looking forward to going there because of her mood swings. But in her stage at this time, I could make her happy and she made me happy. I realized being with her was usually the bright spot of my day, not merely a commitment. I'm sure it would have been different if she was generally non-responsive or not happy with me, but for now it was great. I didn't realize at the time how important this daily interaction was going to be for our deepening relationship that was developing into a revitalized love affair. My perseverance during this time and her preparing her heart ahead of time paid off later down the line.

My intent all along was to make her as happy as possible, regardless of any inconvenience it might cause me. But by taking a break every once in a while, I appreciated my time with her even more. Because I was happier, I'm sure she was happier to be with me. I now felt less guilty when I couldn't be with her.

Who would have guessed that Mary, the one with the problems, the one who needed all the help, would be the one who would put things in perspective and be my salvation for sanity?

My talks with Carol lasted for about a year. It was exactly what I needed at the time and it spurred me on to try to do some things for myself. I learned that while it was important to get out, it wasn't good if it made me feel guilty or I did something by myself that made me feel more isolated…so balance was the key. At the least, these sessions let me vent my true feelings and underlying concerns without dumping on someone closer to me.

With Mary's long-term care needs, finances have been an ongoing concern. I've kept a detailed financial spreadsheet since shortly after Mary went to assisted living, recording every cent spent to see where it all goes on a monthly basis. I'm frugal, if not cheap, to begin with, but by monitoring expenses and saving, I feel I've been doing what I could to help plan for our future.

I went to a financial planner during this time to see what guidance I could glean. He basically told me, "With your uncertainty for the future, there's no way to develop a financial plan for retirement." It never helped when people asked me, "When are you going to retire?" or "Why haven't you retired yet?"

Throughout all this time—during the time when I took care of Mary more and more at home, the dreadful three-month period, and the years she's been at Meadowside—I've worked full-time at the same company. I'm fortunate that my job and management have allowed some flexibility to work occasionally from home, but I've been physically in the office most of the time.

It wasn't a secret at work that Mary had Alzheimer's. People occasionally asked me how she was doing. Sometimes they seemed to show genuine concern, sometimes they asked more out of work etiquette, which was appreciated nonetheless. Some likely avoided the topic as they felt awkward or believed it would be considered prying into my personal matters and not appropriate to discuss in a work environment. Some I'm sure didn't know the situation. So I rarely discussed it.

Mary and I had always attended company holiday parties together, but no one at work really got to know her. Except for one man who retired midway through this time, who I still occasionally meet for lunch, neither we as a couple nor I ever socialized with anyone outside of company functions.

They were friends as work colleagues, and as with any work environment, such "friendships" ran the gamut. They were understanding and accommodating when I needed to take care of something for Mary. But everyone has their own lives and own problems, and there was nothing they could do to help other than allowing me the flexibility I needed on occasion.

A group of five old work colleagues from a previous job—two men and three women—tried to meet for dinner occasionally to catch up on everyone's lives and families. We considered it successful if it worked out once a year. One of them, a female co-worker, and I occasionally met for Saturday brunch in between. One time, the executive director of Mary's residence was at the same restaurant with her family. I introduced the two women to each other and, while I don't feel the director thought anything nefarious was going on, I admit I felt uneasy, wondering what she might be thinking, regardless of the fact that it was an innocent meeting of two friends to talk about what was happening in our lives.

One problem I've personally run into is that it's difficult for the spouse of someone with Alzheimer's to become or remain friends with someone of the opposite sex. Occasionally, while walking Cody in the neighborhood common area, I saw a lady walking her dog. We talked some and once in a while, for a short part of the walk, we walked together to let the dogs do their duty, then went our separate ways. There was nothing more to this. We were just two people walking and talking in public.

However, a neighbor apparently asked her something like, "Is that Mary's husband I saw you walking with?" The lady left me a nice note stating our being seen together could "ruin our Christian witness," as we had discussed that we each attended church. I hardly ever saw her walking her dog after that and talked with her only a couple of times out the window from my car. Our conversations were just two casual acquaintances making "chit-chat" and nothing more. She was easy to talk with in a noncommittal manner with no strings attached, and I needed someone like that at the time. It's too bad some people are quick to cast aspersions and be so judgmental.

I do understand though. I wouldn't want people to think I'm cheating on Mary, nor would I want someone else's reputation to be tainted by her being seen with me. But it's disappointing that people often assume the worst and that, as with the neighbor, busy-body, gossipy speculation can triumph. Unfortunately, it has made me a bit disillusioned with society, since some people seem to enjoy thinking the worst and spreading their "enlightenment." Family caregivers and those most directly affected by Alzheimer's often end up sitting on the sidelines of life, and it's a shame.

Regardless of family, friends, colleagues, the support group and Carol's efforts, it was still easy for me to become isolated. At the beginning of our Alzheimer's journey all was going well, and I felt I could handle everything on my own. After all, Mary was *my* wife, and thus *my* responsibility—the "for better or for worse... in sickness and in health" commitment. But in retrospect, I see how this attitude of trying to do it all alone, when taken to the extreme, can be the start of a downward spiral.

It was ironic, but I guess I had to hit a bottom in my own isolation and grief when trying to ensure Mary's happiness— which led to restoring myself a bit so that I could better achieve what I wanted for Mary. I started to realize I needed to keep the long road in mind, yet I also needed to quit worrying about the things I couldn't do anything about and try to circumvent future worries—to be happy in the present and not lose out on what was around me and in front of me.

And I finally let others in, enough to tone down my obsession about what was best for Mary and focus on both of us—what professionals, my support group, and others with similar experiences all had assured me was best for her and me.

It was like walking a tight-rope sometimes, or maybe juggling, or maybe juggling while walking a tight-rope, keeping a balance in my life while keeping all of the "balls" in the air…"one day at a time" seemed to be my best motto. Some days were better than others.

Chapter 20

Second Guessing Myself

Many guilts, regrets, and "what-ifs" have plagued me over these years.

I was with Mary most of the time when she was sick before those horrendous three months, but I still wondered, *what if I had stayed home with her the whole time? Would things have turned out differently? Would the fears of our house not have spiraled out of control? Would she not have had the severity of her delusions, hallucinations, and different identities?*

I realize I did the best I could by trying to get her help when she started having problems, taking her to all the appropriate doctors and finding her the best facility I could in the area with the time I had.

And yet many questions continued to haunt me. *Should I have been more forceful getting her to a psychiatrist sooner who could meet with her face-to-face, even at the expense of hurting our relationship? Should I not have given in to her resistance?*

Could something different have been done with her psychiatric medications so that she wasn't so sedated at times? The psychiatrist knew her needs better than I did and was following her illness closely, adjusting her medications as he felt appropriate, and I realize it was a delicate balance between her having problems versus her being sedated.

I'm sure this occurs with everyone, but as I look back over my life, there were times I believe things could have, or should have, been handled differently. There's a saying, "No person on their deathbed ever said, 'I wish I had spent more time in the office'." (Heard from Rabbi Harold Kushner; attributed by some to Senator Paul Tsongas.) This certainly has some truth to it, but as with everything, both sides can be carried to extremes.

In retrospect, I wish I had been more leisurely at home over our years together to enjoy life with my wife—that I had spent more time with Mary before rushing off to work, or tried harder to come home from work earlier, or made more effort not to work on a weekend. I regret life was so rushed before her illness and wish we had gone camping more since Mary loved it so much. But when trying to provide for a family and trying to ensure a secure financial future, doing what you feel you need to do at the time often takes precedence…a holdover of what I learned from my dad.

Regardless, Mary doesn't remember those times now, so for the sake of her happiness, it doesn't matter I guess. Today all that matters is one day at a time.

Sometimes I wonder what Mary might really want if she could actually think about it or express it. I never wanted her to feel as if I was abandoning her. Still, her needs had to supersede her wants most of the time, so perhaps it's best I never knew the latter. All I could do was the best I could under the circumstances.

I sometimes thought about what life would have been like if our roles were reversed. *What if I was the one who had Alzheimer's and Mary had to take care of me or make sure I was taken care of?* I know I wouldn't want Mary to have to go through all the stress and work of taking care of me one on one under these circumstances, especially if I was content where I was living in an assisted living community. This thought helped my mental status since I truly believed I would have wanted Mary to do for me what I was doing for her.

It would have been much harder on her if I had been the one to have Alzheimer's since there were new and ongoing expenses, and I brought in all the money and had always handled all financial matters for the family. She would have been overwhelmed if she had to take this over.

Everything being equal, and if there had been a normal slow progression of the disease without the bizarre happenings, I know both of us would have taken care of the other one at home for as long as we physically could. But everything is never equal.

Mary's overall situation in and of itself could be sad and depressing, but the ongoing quandary causing me the most anguish and sleepless nights for the first few years was whether to try to bring her back home to live. I really did miss her, at least her normal self.

This wasn't a dilemma during her first months in assisted living because I assumed she would be there for a relatively short time, while waiting for whatever was causing her psychiatric problems to be brought under control. Until we reached that milestone, there were too many complications to consider bringing her back.

I knew I had done for Mary what was best for her by putting her in Meadowside. But when the psychiatric storm had finally passed and Mary was calmer, happier and more herself, albeit continuing to decline, I started to wonder whether it could work to bring her home again.

She was happy where she was, we had good times together, and bringing her home would probably be for my own peace of mind I rationalized. Still, I felt I had to consider it.

I did not want our years of a loving and happy marriage to end on this note, living apart, if at all possible. It would be like a beautiful symphony being performed, with the audio system starting to distort the sound towards the end, the orchestra forced to continue playing to finish the piece even though it was painful to hear.

So I began doing "little tests" to see if bringing her home again might work. I took "baby steps" at first, taking her on the outings from her residence. While it's true these outings were primarily for both of us to do something different, go out for a change of scenery and have good times together, I always felt I had an underlying intent to see if it could work to bring her home at some time.

Each of our trips to see our family after she started in assisted living were primarily to visit "one last time," but I also knew these were another good way to "test the waters" before seriously considering "taking the plunge" of trying to bring her home.

To further test the waters, I took Mary to our church one Sunday. I wanted to see how she could and would interact with others outside of her residence, especially people she had known. *Would she remember them? How would she interact with them? Would it bring back good memories? Or make her sad?*

I had two big worries going into this venture. One was that she would realize what she was missing out on, that she would know, or at least sense, that her life was not right. The other was that she would recognize some friends who had never visited her and would somehow piece this together, which would only bring sadness. Regardless, I felt I had to try.

I made sure to take her to church on a nice day so the weather wasn't a factor. I let the caregivers know what I was doing so they had her all dressed up, wearing a colorful scarf she always liked, with her hair nicely done and makeup on.

We arrived at the church twenty minutes before the service started so she could see and interact with people. I really didn't think she could make it through the whole service, so I didn't want to take a chance of her not seeing people, and vice versa. Also, this would allow her to enjoy the song part of the service at the beginning that she always loved so much.

As we walked from the parking lot the greeters opened the door. Two people who knew Mary gave her hugs, telling her how happy they were to see her. There wasn't a lot of reaction from Mary but she seemed to enjoy it, putting her arms around one of the ladies' waists returning the hug, not unlike what she might do with one of the caregivers or me.

It wasn't a very big church, but we stood in the back of the sanctuary to ensure people would see us. As those who knew Mary saw her, most came over to say hello and gave her a hug, trying to talk with her saying, "It's so good to see you." Some asked her questions like, "How are you doing?" By this time her verbal skills had declined, so there was little response. I knew going into it that she wouldn't be able to really talk with them, but I felt the familiar faces (if she still recognized them), the smiles, the hugs, the emotions would supervene to make it a pleasant experience.

I had wanted to see her broadcast a big smile, or any smile, when she saw old friends there...like she often showed when she saw the caregivers at assisted living. But this didn't happen. Outwardly, she didn't seem to remember any of the church people much if at all.

When it was time for the service to start, we sat in the back row, which I had planned to do...just in case. The worship service was typical for when she had attended there, most of the songs being ones that would have been familiar to her. I kept sneaking looks at her out of the corner of my eye, hoping to see the loving, lost-in-the-moment smile she used to have as she sang and signed with the songs. Much to my disappointment, outwardly she seemed to get nothing out of the song service.

We stood the whole song service which she could easily do at this stage, but she kept wanting to walk around during the regular service that followed, which became a distraction. While it didn't seem to bother the pastor, some others understandably looked uncomfortable, and when she actually started walking out of our row of seats it seemed best to leave…so I followed her and we just kept walking out the door.

Overall the whole venture was too much for her to process and didn't seem enjoyable. But interestingly, once we were in the car I asked her, "Did you like coming to church?"

She said, "Yes," without hesitation.

"Would you like to come back sometime?"

"Yes, I would like that," she responded.

Taking her to our church was something I felt I had to try, as it would have just been something else I would have felt guilty about if I hadn't attempted it. But I knew I likely wouldn't do it again.

I decided as another strategy to start taking her to the apartment where Jeff and his wife, Ashley, lived several times for dinner. These outings worked well. We had a good time, and she was okay with leaving and going back to Meadowside. The biggest problem we had was after we left their apartment one time. There was a cold, drizzling rain, so they didn't walk us to our car. I had parked as close as possible to their apartment in the large parking lot.

We walked to the curb, but I could not convince Mary to step off the curb to get to our car in the parking lot. We tried several other places along the curb, but she wouldn't take the step. We needed to walk to the opposite corner of the lot where there was a slope leading off a sidewalk. This worked.

For future visits Jeff went out with us and, together, we were able to convince her, with help, to step off the curb. I'm sure this resistance was out of fear or a lack of spatial perception, as opposed to obstinance. This unwillingness to take one small step down started to occur regularly, which greatly hampered our ability to go places that weren't totally flat.

I also took her to a close-by lake several times. She had always liked to walk down to the lake where we used to kayak. There was a small hump at the edge of the parking lot, less than an inch high, to divert rainwater from running down the paved paths. Walking back to the car one time, I could not convince her to step over that small rise. We had to walk to the other side of the lot to get back to the car.

To make things worse, she became hesitant about stepping across expansion joints in sidewalks when there was the slightest unevenness or change in the type of pavement, such as from concrete to brick, even if the surface was level. One time it took several attempts, much coaching, and some gentle tugging to convince her to step off a quarter-inch rubber mat onto the surrounding floor.

These outings and trips were a good way for Mary to become used to going places with me, but they didn't answer how she would react going back to our house. I was hesitant to take her home for a long time. She was happy in assisted living, then memory care, and I knew in my heart she was better off there. I certainly didn't want to cause her any harm or bring back memories that might make her want to stay at the house, or miss home more, unless it seemed it could work. I didn't know, and was admittedly afraid to know, what she might remember or realize.

But with the final visits to Jeff's turning out successfully (except for the curb thing), I finally mustered the courage to take her back to our house for the first time. I wanted to bring her home, at least for a visit. And I wanted to finally overcome my doubts and fears.

I made dinner and I made sure Jeff and Ashley joined us and were there before I arrived with Mary.

Upon entering the front door, Cody greeted her immediately, wagging his tail in delight. Mary glanced down briefly, saying, "What a nice puppy," but had no meaningful reaction or apparent remembrance.

She also appeared to have no recognition of the kitchen. I guided her into our family room, where there were photos and various memorable items, especially on the mantle. We had a pleasant conversation, but she had nothing to say about the house or what was in it, and she didn't focus on anything in particular.

Sitting at the table during dinner, Cody was right next to Mary, waiting for her to drop some food. He even put his nose on Mary's leg like his mother had done when we met the two of them in the garage to pick him up and take him home. At that time it melted Mary's heart; this time she paid him no attention. She didn't remember him.

She had no apparent recognition of anything or seemed to feel any differently being at our house than she did going to Jeff's or being at Meadowside. It seemed like it was just another place for her—not the home where we had spent the last eight years of our lives together before Meadowside.

On the other hand, my emotions were all over the place. I was relieved she didn't become upset or say she wanted to stay or refused to leave. At the same time, I was sad she didn't seemingly remember or recognize anything.

There were two steps up to the front porch of our house. While she didn't resist much when she came in, Jeff and I had to convince Mary to step down when we left to take her back to Meadowside.

At subsequent dinners, it went from difficult to impossible to convince her to step up or down those two steps. Jeff and I needed to be on each side of her, holding her arms and lifting her up, once we convinced her to cooperate with us. I could never get her to take these steps by myself. I eventually built an eight-foot ramp in the garage to circumvent the steps, which worked well for navigating them.

I compiled a list of the pros and cons of Mary staying in assisted living versus her living at home with help. It became complicated thinking about all the practical matters: her needing to ascend and descend the stairs, whether she would cooperate with using a lift chair on the stairs, our being able to walk the dog, finding appropriate help Mary would accept, being able to keep my job, et cetera.

The list of pros in favor of her staying in assisted living was long. There they took care of all of her medical needs, blood work, medications, toileting, bathing, meals, activities—in fact, all of her other needs period.

Her residence had a back-up generator and was on a priority list for refueling, so there was always light and heat during the winter. Electricity usually went off sometimes at our house, and it became cold, and would likely be scary for her in the dark.

Safety was always a concern. With her being somewhat overweight now, I could not pick her up if she fell, and she wasn't able to help.

I also had to admit I wasn't getting any younger. Periodic physical problems on my part could also hamper my being able to take care of her. For a few weeks I had tendonitis in my elbow, resulting in it being painful even to pick up a cup or grip anything. Another time I had groin pain for several weeks during which I couldn't bend over to pick something up or get out of a chair without pain. There's no way I could have taken care of Mary's needs during these times.

She could not follow simple instructions and often put items in her mouth or walked in the wrong direction, so I also realized she would need constant attention and watching. It was raining when I took her to the dentist one time. I knew we would get drenched with her walking so slowly, so I told her to stay where she was under the covered area at the facility while I ran to bring the car, which was not far away and in sight. It took maybe thirty seconds for me to run to the car and bring it to pick her up. In the meantime, she had started walking in the opposite direction in the rain. Her not being able to follow simple instructions, much less let logic come into play, was a definite negative for the checklist of reasons why she should come home.

There were some phases of her illness when she wouldn't let me help her, refusing to let me brush her teeth, or especially floss, which was aggravating to both of us. Plus, she had refused to take her medications from me in the past. All of this made me realize she might likely go through even more radical phases, and her moods could change on a moment's notice. There was no real reason to think her fears and irrational behaviors would start up again, but I had no idea what triggered them in the first place. Although she had settled into a "routine" cognitive state, there were fluctuations at this stage, and I never knew what might happen or how she might react negatively in a particular situation.

Mary never had any problem returning to her residence after visiting back "home." When we were able to talk about it, she said she really liked where she was living and wanted to stay there. This was where she felt the most comfortable.

Still, this was hard. Occasionally Mary made a reference to "home," at times even saying, "I want to go home." I initially assumed she was talking about our house when she mentioned it, which caused me a lot of anguish. In her very early days in assisted living, I'm sure this is what she was thinking. Later in memory care, it seemed she was verbalizing more of a random thought, like she often did with other words or phrases, or possibly she heard someone else say it. I could never be sure though.

Making the list of pros and cons was helpful, but I still wavered back and forth. With my primary goal of wanting to make her happy, bringing her home was a continual internal conflict, regardless of what might be better for her—or me—in the long run.

She was happy at the residence and loved the staff. Sometimes when she saw the caregivers, it was like she saw an old friend she hadn't seen for a long time. The exuberant expressions on her face—smiling, eyes bright, sometimes with her mouth open in happy amazement—said it all. As I was walking around with her, there were stages she often gravitated away from me and toward one of the staff with a smile and hug. There's no way she would have been as happy with one outside person—even if it was me.

All the constant fretting over whether it could possibly work to bring her home was very draining emotionally. My talking through the situation and possibilities with professionals and my Alzheimer's support group, detailing my quandary and discussing the various pros and cons, led to everyone—with one exception—telling me that bringing her home was definitely a bad idea. Several bluntly stated I would be stupid to try it, as it would not be good for either Mary or me, either for the short term or long run. All this I knew, but it was reassuring to have confirmation from others who knew what it was like.

The one exception was a caregiver who took care of Mary a lot during her first few months in assisted living, during a time when Mary was sometimes sad and cried at night after I left. This caregiver was concerned and comforted Mary as much as possible. I'm sure she didn't know all my wife and I had gone through or the fact that Mary was still having some of her psychiatric problems that likely only I still noticed. I know this caregiver had the best of intentions for Mary and believed she was looking out for Mary's happiness. But her telling me I should take Mary home added immensely to my guilt, made me question all over again whether I should try it for a few months, and sent me reeling back to my doubts for a time.

She just didn't know what I had been through so far. I comforted myself, trying to stay solid in my decision once I made it. *What if something happened to me and once Mary got home she needed to return to the residential facility? Wouldn't that be worse than never bringing her home in the first place?*

There was little doubt bringing her home would lead to additional work, stress, and health problems for me. She would take all my time and attention, and I could never leave her alone. No doubt I would sleep even less, especially since I wouldn't feel good about taking medicine to help me sleep in which case I might not wake up if she needed something. My job would certainly suffer over time. Financial costs of in-home care compared to the residence were calculated, and I needed to keep working either way. It could be a self-perpetuating calamity for both of us.

There was an ongoing conflict within me, knowing bringing her home would be a lose-lose situation. Yet still I agonized for several years over whether or not to try it.

Chapter 21

Being There

For the time being at least, I decided to keep Mary at Meadowside and, as it turned out, she continued to slowly decline in memory care, so I realize it ended up being the best decision after all. A lot started changing with respect to what we did together as well.

I still visited her every day unless there was a reason I couldn't while still working forty to sometimes sixty-plus hours a week. Since time was so limited, I felt I needed to make the most of each visit. Jeff often visited if I was unable to and called me to talk with her while he was there. If neither of us could make it, I usually called the residence and they handed her the phone to talk with me. These calls were always short and superficial, since she was less and less able to carry on any real conversation as time went on. Of course, the calls weren't like a visit. Sometimes they went well, whereas other times it would likely have been better not to have called.

The typical phone call early on went something like this: "Hi Mary. This is Marc."

"Hi."

"Did you have a good day?

"Yes, I had a good day."

"I'm out of town on a trip and can't come see you tonight, but I wanted to call and talk with you."

Sometimes she said something, sometimes not.

I'd close it with, "I love you and I'll see you soon. Bye."

Usually she responded with an "Okay" or "Bye."

In the later years, her usual response might start with, "Hi," but then she would start humming with no further words. Sometimes she started humming when I told her who I was, which was nice since I knew she recognized my voice and was happy at the time.

It was becoming more and more difficult to tell if she realized when I missed a day. Very early on, she sometimes asked me on a phone call, "Where are you?" and I told her if she asked. On trips lasting more than a day or two, I was told Mary occasionally asked, "Where is he?" Of course, this made me feel good she missed me, but guilty about taking the trip, even though it was usually out of necessity.

Sometimes when I arrived, she was still being taken care of in her room after dinner. I often waited at the other end of the hallway and talked with other residents. When I saw her come down the hall, I started walking towards her with my arms stretched out. During the earlier years, once she recognized me, she picked up speed towards me, almost running at times, with a big smile followed by a nice hug. This was great for both of us, and the caregivers seemed uplifted by this reaction and interaction.

Hardly ever was she not happy to see me, and never was she upset that I came (except rarely during the difficult period when we were getting her psychiatric symptoms under control).

There were phases though when she really seemed to recognize her plight. At these times she was very huggy, she cried

263

a little and said, "I'm sorry. I'll stay here." She really seemed to know what was happening to her. She was deeply sad and very loving at these periods. I stayed longer to get her through these times until her mood was more lighthearted and normal.

I'll admit, I had conflicting thoughts at times about going to see her, especially before her psychiatric symptoms were controlled or when she was over-sedated with the medications and "out of it." Occasionally, my hesitation related more to scheduling the time because I had so much to do for work once I got home. This was a real conflict for me, but her wanting me and needing me always won out. I wanted to make her as happy as possible, and certainly did not want her to feel abandoned. It was an ongoing debate in my head during the early years.

My routine of staying at work until after she ate dinner and was taken care of as needed worked well, but sometimes it forced me to stay later at work than I otherwise would have. It would have taken too long and been a waste of valuable time to go home in between. I didn't feel resentment, but it was an inconvenience that interfered with my having a more normal life.

Since I was somewhat co-dependent and a people pleaser, her mood and how she received me often affected my overall mood. While I tried not to let my disappointment show to her, it negatively affected the rest of my day when she wasn't outwardly happy to see me. When Mary was happy—and happy with me—I was happy. And when she wasn't, I wasn't.

One time I arrived, I could tell she was bothered and sad, nearly crying. I almost dreaded going over to her in case it might be something related to me, or I'd find she was experiencing a keener awareness of her situation. But of course I wanted to help if I could, so I took a deep breath and approached her as she sat on a chair in the middle of the common area.

I knelt in front of her, took her hand, stroked her cheek with my other hand so she looked up to see me, and asked, "What's wrong Mary?"

She answered in a teary voice, "My dad died," which had occurred many years before.

I simply replied in a sympathetic voice, "I'm very sorry. Let's take a walk and talk about it if you want."

She said, "Thank you," and that was the end of her being upset. She was in positive spirits afterwards and we had a good time together. I learned not to assume she was just sad or try to guess why, or even try to fix it, but to merely help her move forward.

My visits were usually rather lengthy except for rare occasions she was non-responsive when nothing seemed to help and my trying to interact with her seemed more aggravating than helpful to her. Later on, she seemed to recognize me more, I think partially because I was there every day at the same time. Having a regular routine for visiting helped.

I always tried to come in with a smile and cheery voice and be happy to see her. I often told her, "I came to see you as soon as I got off work," which likely resonated in her long-term memory since she knew I had done this since we first married. I always took her hand and we strolled away from others before we hugged so we did not embarrass anyone.

If she wasn't sitting with others when I walked in, once I saw her I sometimes said in an excited voice, "I found you. I'm so glad I found you." She always smiled at this. Early on, she used to say, "I found you" when she first saw me.

When she was more aware of her circumstances, I had to maintain a difficult balance when I arrived between appearing too happy, in which case she might think I was happy (or at least not sad) about our situation, versus being too solemn and bringing us both down. It didn't take too long to develop a good balance and yet be flexible depending on her status and mood at the time. Later on, it was definitely good for both of us for me to go in happy and ready to lift her spirits for a good time with her.

There were isolated times she was unsettled when I arrived, saying, "I have to go. I've got to go now."

At first, I asked her where she needed to go, but she didn't know. The best response was, "Okay, let's go together."

She usually said, "Okay." I took her hand, started walking down the hall, and that was the end of it.

We walked a lot, holding hands, often with our fingers interlocked. Occasionally, she held onto my arm. We said "lovey" things that (hopefully) no one else could hear.

The caregivers and other staff were always helpful during my visits. Everyone knew Mary by name, including kitchen, cleaning, maintenance, and administrative staff. They almost always at least smiled and said hello, calling her by name as they passed by, and often paused for a brief chat, or in the case of the caregivers, sometimes giving her a hug.

A couple of children, a boy and girl maybe six to eight years old, sometimes visited memory care to visit their grandparent. Mary enjoyed watching and playing a game of hide-and-seek with them. They hid behind a chair and jumped out, then Mary got excited and laughed and often became more vocal. Both the children and Mary got a big kick out of it.

I often wanted to do something active with my wife, thinking she would want to "do" something with me. Sometimes I think I pushed her too much or tried to be in a hurry. One mistake I made was to walk too fast for her, sometimes walking ahead of her to try to pull her along a little, which was likely frustrating for her. I learned to slow down and let her set the pace.

But later on, if I didn't lead her along on a walk, we likely wouldn't go anywhere. Even then, I tried to walk beside her by holding our hands out in front of us to lead her on. What worked best when it was feasible was for me to walk backwards while holding both her hands and looking at her face.

One time I knew I needed to leave before I normally left for a work dinner. In all my wisdom, to make up for a shorter visit I tried to include the same amount of walking, hugging and singing as usual. I tried to pack too much in, and it was too rushed and harried. This was not good and was unsettling for both of us. For us, it was better to take it slow and easy, regardless of the length of the visit.

I eventually learned to calm down and slow down before going in to see her, regardless of how my day was at work, how much more I needed to do once I left her, or what was on my mind with other stresses and obligations. I needed to be unconditionally patient and not appear rushed. With this attitude, we could just enjoy each other's company.

Whenever she seemed unsettled or distressed, distraction worked well, whether singing, dancing, hugging, getting her to "help" the staff do something, or whatever seemed appropriate based on who was there and what was going on. Something familiar like the little tune we made up had a calming effect on her. Humming took little or no thought and made her smile as we walked.

I wanted to leave each visit on a good note. Her last impression of me as I left each day was likely what she would remember the best, or at least have lingering feelings of, until I returned, so I wanted each day to be a special day—for both of us.

The process was by trial and error, and it was difficult for me to figure how to end my visits as she went through different phases during the first couple of years. Upon leaving, I almost always said, "I'll come back to see you tomorrow as soon as I get off work," whether the next day was a workday or not. This seemed to help set a good routine or expectation for her.

Sometimes it was easy to leave. She acknowledged I needed to go and smiled, and was okay with my saying, "I'll see you tomorrow."

Sometimes she responded with, "I'll be here," or "Okay, I'll stay here," which was not stated in a nasty or "guilt trip" manner.

I often replied, "Good, that way I'll know exactly where to find you!"

Sometimes I asked her in an upbeat tone, "Can I come back tomorrow?"

She almost always responded with a nice, "Yes." At those times, I left feeling good.

A few times she seemed to get teary and said, "I want to stay here," as if she thought we were both going to leave. It was good to hear she liked and accepted where she lived, and at this stage I tried hard not to take it as a negative towards me.

One time when I had to leave, she said, "Go play," which made me think she thought I was leaving her to go have fun. I left that night feeling terrible, but the next night as I left, she said, "I'll go play." So it didn't have anything to do with my leaving after all. I generally tried not to take what she said to heart—too much.

There were certain actions that seemed to trigger a more negative (or at least not positive) reaction from her when it was closing in on the time for me to leave. We could be having a great time together, and then we often went into the main community area where the TV, or sometimes music, was always on at that time of the evening. We used to sit down around the time an evening snack and juice were being served to everyone. This seemed to be a trigger for Mary to start to shut down or become indifferent towards me, like she knew this was the beginning of my exit. What I don't know is how it would have been different if I had stayed longer, but by that time she had already made up her mind that, while not necessarily being outwardly upset, she was not going to be outwardly happy about it. Leaving on this note was distressing to me the rest of the evening.

The next day I would often ask the staff who were working the evening before if she was okay after I left, and they always said she was fine. Still, a good approach I learned that worked well at that stage was to leave Mary before she was seated for the evening. I left when she was engaged with, or at least next to, one of the caregivers, for example "helping" them get snacks together or fold napkins. I told her I'd be back tomorrow, and they took her over to sit with the others a short time later. Leaving her with a caregiver worked well as it wasn't my simply saying good-bye and leaving her without someone to interact with. On occasion, she pinched my cheek or gently grabbed my nose and smiled as I said my final goodbye.

Once our goodbye system was established, Mary appeared content almost all of the time. It seemed she really wanted to stay. This was her home now.

And yet, although she was generally very happy and our interactions were usually great, there could be setbacks from time to time, and the reason was usually not evident. It grieved me when Mary was unsettled over something—whether real or imagined—but especially if it seemed to be about my leaving. If she was distressed and couldn't say why, I tried to let it go and just be with her, which usually helped. On the bright side, I knew she wouldn't remember the bad times, so this made them a little more bearable. Luckily, they didn't happen often, and each day was a new day.

I thought more people would have visited Mary in assisted living and memory care. Most people have well wishes and seemingly good intentions but following through is difficult for a variety of reasons. Regretfully, except for Jeff, all relatives on both sides of our family lived long distances away. Jeff visited her some, and David almost every day whenever he traveled to our area.

This made me realize how imperative it is to develop a good group of close friends well before something significant like an illness arises. Our moving several times to different states hindered developing these important long-term relationships.

I often thumbed through the visitor sign-in book at the facility to see if anyone had been there who I wasn't aware of. I think most people let me know if they stopped by or planned to visit her, but thumbing through the pages of the sign-in log over the years and rarely seeing Mary's name was discouraging.

Understandably, some people don't want to visit people who are "different" or sick or dying—whether their illnesses are sudden or slowly develop from a disease like Alzheimer's. It can be awkward, even scary, and people often don't know what to do or say. I know, because I was one of them. With Alzheimer's, it could be even more difficult since a visitor can't accurately know what the person remembers or comprehends.

When possible, I tried to talk with potential visitors to let them know what to expect to dispel some of the uncertainty on their parts, and how to best interact with her physically and verbally, which varied a lot over the years. This helped the visits that did occur to be more positive for both Mary and the family or friends who stopped in to see her, but who may have stopped coming if the get-togethers were too uncomfortable. However it turned out though, any visit was better than none.

Chapter 22

Conquering Communication

As Mary's verbal abilities declined over time, my ways to communicate with her required changes, both verbal and nonverbal. Her physical needs were taken care of by the facility's staff, so the cornerstone of Mary's happiness seemed to be her feeling loved, not only by her residence caregivers but by me. Subtle differences in what was said or especially how it was said often made a big difference.

I wanted Mary to communicate as well as possible for as long as possible, so I encouraged her to talk in whatever manner she could and felt like doing at the time. I asked her simple questions and encouraged her to ask questions, always answering them and making her feel good about it.

Over time, what she tried to say had less and less meaning with respect to word choice, syntax, context or even overall understandability. Fortunately, there was some improvement after all of her psychotropic medications were discontinued. At that point, she was not sedated, and was more responsive and "with it."

One time, she distinctly said, somewhat sadly, but more matter of fact, "I wish things could be different." It was difficult to know what she really realized about her current condition or her future, but I'm sure she knew to some degree.

A couple of times in earlier assisted living, she cried and said, "I don't know what's happening to me." She had made similar statements while at home. Early in memory care, we were walking down the hall holding hands and she said solemnly, while looking down, "This isn't how I imagined our later years together."

Each of these times, I looked into her eyes and said some variation of, "I know. This isn't what I thought it would be like either (*or* I wish it could be different also), but we'll make the best of it and get through this together."

These times were not only sad for me but very frustrating internally. I've always been a problem solver, whether at work, around the house, or with Mary. This mindset wasn't always the best in our relationship throughout the years because if there was an issue of some sort, I always wanted to *fix* it, whereas all she wanted to do was *talk* about it. These current situations were not ones I could resolve, like I always tried to do, and digging any deeper into details behind Mary's statements would only have made things worse.

On occasion, she asked me, "How are you doing?" and seemed to mean it and want an answer.

I answered with, "I'm doing okay. We're with each other every day, and this is a nice place. You like and love the people here, and they like and love you. And we love each other. That makes all the difference." I always tried to focus on the positive.

Other times she randomly started making somewhat coherent statements or asking more meaningful questions, but then drifted into talking about something else, singing or humming. Her attention span sometimes didn't allow a thought to be carried to completion.

She liked me to tell her, "I like you," or "I love you," or "I'm really happy to see you." But *showing* her I cared and loved her, with hand-holding and hugs, were what she liked and needed most.

At this stage, I never brought up the fact, and we never discussed, she had Alzheimer's, and I'm not sure if she even realized it. But she did understand enough to know there was a problem, and she sometimes said, "I'm sorry." This statement seemed a general feeling and was never in response to anything specific. She couldn't express why she was sorry, but it seemed she was apologizing for the situation in which we found ourselves. It stressed her when she thought she had let someone down.

These times of realization caused a lot of stress and sadness for both of us.

I would tell her, "I'm very sorry also, but you have nothing to be sorry about. Please know that you didn't do anything wrong. Nothing is your fault. We're both in this together." This was usually the end of this topic in our conversation—until the next time it arose again. Just being with her seemed to be the best thing I could do.

Mary always appreciated what people did for her and usually had something nice to say to the staff such as, "Thank you," or "That's nice," or "You're a nice lady." Oftentimes these responses were totally appropriate to the situation or conversation. Other times they weren't.

For example, a caregiver might ask, "How are you feeling today Mary?" which she answered with a "That's nice" response. I recall a couple of times Mary was standing close to several caregivers who were talking, saying something to Mary to include her. She couldn't follow what they were talking about but would insert her input with, "You're a nice lady."

Still, I believe Mary's pleasant responses showed what was deep in her heart that she had prepared for so many years.

It was important to keep conversations simple and basic. I don't want to demean Mary but communicating with her was often like talking with a child, though not in a childish manner. It's just that conversation needed to be kept simple, and she primarily needed to be constantly reassured she was safe and everything was okay.

On rare occasions, Mary mentioned something about dying. What she realized was uncertain as she usually didn't seem worried, and I didn't want to pursue any negative topics. To be honest, I wasn't sure I wanted to know how much she realized. The times she eluded to dying were way more distressing for me than they were for her.

One time early in memory care, out of the blue as we were walking down the hall to her room for some alone time, she said, "I don't want to die," and seemed to fully comprehend what she was saying, a sad look shadowing her eyes which seemed darker than usual.

This took me by surprise, but I tried to reassure her as best as I could. "I don't want you to die either. You're doing well and not about to die." This seemed to help and, along with an all-healing hug, in a flash the sadness in her seemed to pass, like a gray cloud moving past the sun.

One time she looked at me gravely, put her hand on my cheek, and said, "Don't die," in a serious tone. It was stated so clearly and meaningfully that it triggered multiple reactions within me, mostly my distress that she worried about such matters. It was a real dilemma for me—wanting her to be mentally aware for as long as possible yet wanting her to get beyond such depressing thoughts…but the latter might mean she was declining which I didn't want. I'm sure I stressed over all of this more than Mary did since these moments were short-lived for her. Such instances added to my mission to make her happy. Whether her comment was self-serving since she liked my visits or out of real concern for my well-being (which was her true nature) is unknown, but I think likely both.

I assured her with, "I'm okay, I have no intention of dying any time soon, and I promise to take care of you forever and ever." I knew she needed to hear this over and over, since she likely didn't remember the words from one minute to the next.

During such serious times, it was difficult to know what to say or how to act or react, so sometimes we just hugged to console each other.

Luckily these depressing discussions were not the norm and we usually had good times and conversations. I remember a time we were looking at a painting of three cute puppies on the wall of the memory care unit as we walked around. I asked her what she thought would be good names for them but got no response. So I asked, "How about Flopsy, Mopsy and Cottontail?" She grinned broadly and then we both started laughing.

Another time Mary and I were facing each other. She was talking and singing, but most of it was nonsensical, or at least unintelligible to me. All of a sudden, she said, "And you wore the horse's head." There was a dead silence, we looked at each other, and both of us burst out laughing.

I always hated the times we were with each other in silence for what seemed a long time because I couldn't think of anything appropriate to say. I think she was fine with it, and I learned it was often better to be silent—but physically interactive with her—than to say something just to say something, realizing this made the more nonverbal times easier. With time, due to her decreased capability to verbally communicate, little if anything was said if I didn't start a "conversation." She seemed to like our talking though in whatever form, so I was rarely silent for very long.

We spoke a lot about what we could see around us, but later our talks mostly evolved to how much we liked and loved each other, or how nice it was where she lived.

We called relatives together and she always enjoyed this. There was often a long silence when Mary was on the phone with David. Sometimes, even though I knew better, I would ask if she was still "talking" with him and she would nod, assuring me she was. Just knowing he was on the other end of the line seemed comforting to her—kind of like being with him. At times, she seemed to be singing to him.

I developed a mental list of what she liked to talk about, could usually comprehend, and what were "safe" or at least innocuous topics. Some of the items on my list included what we saw in nature, her personal appearance, something or someone being particularly nice where she lived, a good dinner or snack, a pretty picture on the wall, our sons and their families.

A continual dilemma was deciding what to tell her or remind her about regarding our previous life together. *Should I talk with her about the house (our home), family members, deaths in the family, Cody, neighbors, church?* I would ask myself. There was constant conflict inside me over not knowing what to tell her or show her. *Might it bring back memories that could lead to her being less happy with her present situation, or even cause various fears to return?*

On one hand, I wanted to involve her with people and life events, but I don't recall her ever asking a question about anyone or anything that was happening on the outside. On the other, I didn't want to remind her of what she was missing out on that might make her feel unhappy. I also didn't want to remind her of people who didn't visit her, not wanting her to think she was forgotten or not meaningful to them any longer. People often asked me how Mary was doing and asked me to tell her hello, which I stopped doing if they didn't visit her or the message would no longer mean anything to her.

What to tell her was a difficult balance that I often fretted over. I usually erred on the conservative side, not telling her too much since she was happy as she was. *Why ruin it by making her miss something or someone?* It was much better for her if I focused on the positives of her present, which included doing things with her, taking her out for drives or bringing special items to her.

Over time, I did learn that reality was not always good—for either of us—and actual lying was not only okay, but merciful. I tried hard not to lie to her for my own psyche, so I often skirted the whole truth and erred on the side of omission. I stopped mentioning things from the past which she could no longer do, such as out-of-town family events or my company's annual party she always enjoyed. I tried to protect her from knowing details that might make her life less happy.

It was not only good, but necessary, to be selective in what I told Mary. It depended a lot on what she could comprehend and if it would make any real difference if she knew the information. For example, Mary and my mother were very close. While in assisted living and into early memory care, we talked with my mother many days, and Mary loved it.

But I never told Mary when my mother passed away. I went to the funeral in Texas, telling her I needed to go on a trip for a few days. She never asked why I needed to go, and she never mentioned my mother again. Whether Mary forgot about my mother doesn't matter. The point is that it would have made her sad if I told her about my mother passing away. She didn't need to know, and with her memory, it didn't make any difference. I felt it was better to leave her with good thoughts, or at least pleasant feelings, about my mother.

When I showed her family photos, pointing out who was in them, she usually didn't look at them other than give them a glance. It seemed a person had to be physically in sight for her to relate.

Many times, I would have loved to talk with her like we had done for so many years. Of course, I knew she couldn't comprehend, so it would be meaningless to her and likely increase her confusion, and thus decrease her happiness.

Similar to not rushing my visits, it helped immensely not to hurry our conversations. I found using a calm, slow, soft-spoken voice was always best, unless I was joking or exaggerating. Mary felt any hurriedness or impatience in my voice, and it affected her in a negative way. I learned that if I needed to leave her earlier than usual to go to my support group or a business dinner, I couldn't just spring it on her at the last minute, or she would become distressed with little reaction or even acknowledgment, clamming up verbally. It usually took me fifteen minutes to gently proceed through an exit strategy.

While talking with Mary, I had to try to relate to what she was experiencing and be on her side. If she was having a problem, I was her ally to help determine how we could handle it together.

If she was fearful, I would commiserate. "I'm worried someone is going to get hurt," she would say.

I usually asked, "Do you know who might get hurt?"

"No, I just feel it's going to happen."

"Okay, I'll look into it and take care of it." This usually quickly solved her immediate concern.

I learned to ask her simple yes/no questions, like, "Would you like to walk around the building?" or "Would you like to take a drive?" Not, "Would you like to walk around the building or take a drive?" Once she answered, I often told her it was a good idea, as if she had suggested it. Asking her to make a decision was too demanding and made her feel uncomfortable, if not inadequate.

Another way I involved her verbally was whenever something special was happening at her place. I often said something like, "Thank you for letting me come to your party. I had a great time." I believe this let her feel more involved and an integral part of what was going on around her, and not merely an occupant or observer.

"Thank you," she would say with a grateful smile.

It was necessary to always be positive and offer Mary reassurance. I told her "You did good," or, "You look nice today," or, "You're pretty," or, "Thanks," with a smile. She seemed to especially appreciate my telling her, "I'm very proud of you."

She always smiled and said, "Thank you," and often told me, "You're a nice man."

Especially as time went on, I discovered giving her a response was usually more important than the response itself. Our banter usually went like this:

"I can't do it." … "That's okay, let's do it together."

"I can't find it." … "We can look for it together."

"We need to open the doors soon." … "Yeah, we'll open them in a little while."

"What is it?" … "I think it's okay."

"What's that one?" … "It's a good one."

"Where are they?" … "They'll be here soon."

"Did I do it?" … "Did you need to do it?" (affirming she did a good job if so.)

"Do I need to do it?" … "Do you want to do it?" (If "yes," "Well, let's go do it together." If "no," "Well, that's good, because you don't need to do it.")

"Did I eat it?" … "Yes, you did, and you liked it!"

If something regarding time … "We have plenty of time."

"Let's do it." or "Do you want to do it?" ... "Okay, let's go do it."

"I don't have any more." ... "That's okay, you don't need any more." Or "I have enough for both of us." Or "Okay, then I'll get you some more."

If she seemed to be talking about something that could be seen that I couldn't understand, I often responded with something like, "Yes, it's very pretty (or nice) isn't it?" A simple "That's nice" usually worked too as well as "Yeah," "Okay," "That's right," "Uh huh," and "I think so." Sometimes no response was needed as she started walking down the hallway or humming before I could respond, and that was the end of it.

It was important to stay away from negatives, and certainly not to cause any negatives. I made sure I didn't say "Don't do that," unless it was something she needed to stop doing that could be potentially dangerous, like putting something in her mouth, or on rare occasions something that was aggravating to others. At those times, I always tried to say whatever I had to in a nice voice. My tone meant everything.

Redirecting her was always better and usually worked. There was a period she often took a lot of items out of the glove compartment when we drove around. While this was somewhat inconvenient, I let her do it, and at the end of the drive I stated, "Let's put them back so we'll have them the next time we go for a drive." She was happy with that and would allow me to put them back.

Sometimes in the residence she stood close or directly in front of the community TV. Of course, this blocked others' views of the screen and could be aggravating, so if I walked in at that time, I went to her saying, "Let's go for a walk." Mary and the others appreciated this.

Since she often couldn't fully comprehend what was stated, it was often good to exaggerate expressions for emphasis.

"That's a *very* beautiful sunset."

"I'm *really* glad to see you."

"You look *very* pretty today."

Sometimes she was exuberantly happy, like she had taken an energy pill or even a silly pill. At these times she was more "verbal," she spoke faster and louder and was more playful. She could be acutely expressive in her intonation. If she had something good to eat during these times and I asked her if it was good, she might smile, open her eyes wide, and say, "Very good...mmm."

The most significant change—for both of us—was transitioning from verbal to mostly nonverbal communication. There were pros and cons to each. Verbal talking was more "normal" and could convey ideas better in both directions, but it took effort and could be frustrating for both of us.

As Mary's Alzheimer's got worse, she seemed happier with nonverbal communication like singing, humming, hugging, touching, making faces, whatever seemed appropriate—all ways of communicating our feelings without words. It was easier, but sometimes not as effective, especially if she or I needed to express a particular thought. On the other hand, we could express ourselves much better in some ways.

As she progressed through memory care, I was often unable to convey any points, much less have a meaningful verbal communication. She never totally lost the ability to use words, but whenever she initiated a conversation it was often unintelligible, except for the times she said something like "I love you" or "I like you." Some of the individual words were understandable but made no sense the way she combined them. I never said anything like, "I'm sorry, I can't understand what you're asking," unless my inability to answer her question was upsetting her, which rarely happened. The time arrived when she could usually answer only simple (mostly yes/no) questions, then even that gradually subsided.

Eventually our communication got to a point where I didn't have to try to determine what she was saying or asking. Within a moment after she began to say or ask something, she often started singing or humming without finishing the thought or expecting any response. Over time she went from singing known songs to humming her own made-up tunes. Her own melodies were initially more complex rhythms but gradually become simpler and more repetitive. Eventually she mostly went back and forth between two notes.

I needed to reassess my means of connecting—if not communicating in the classical sense—with her, which became more physical and visual than verbal. She needed to feel comfortable in her surroundings. This required my abandoning preconceived notions of how I wanted our interactions to be and meet her where she was, not where I wanted her to be.

I learned to listen to her differently, trying hard to discern the feelings behind what she was trying to say—not a bad idea I could have applied better throughout our life together! Communicating nonverbally, like humming our special tune together, was often deeper than talking. This worked well when attempts with words were lost. Whenever there seemed to be an awkward moment developing, I started humming the tune, Mary joined in, and all was well.

I imagine in Mary's mind, her humming helped her to not feel alone. It was her way of "talking"—whether there was anyone to talk with or not. There were times she was humming when I arrived, did so the entire time I was there, and continued as I was leaving. She usually smiled as she was humming. She was happy internally even if she didn't know why—there didn't need to be a reason—and that was fine by me.

Nonverbal gestures and exaggerations were needed more and more for emphasis, such as outstretched arms for a big hug. We frequently teased and laughed, often at silly things like when I pretended to bump my head on a decoration hanging from the ceiling, appearing to be knocked back by it. Making Mary smile and laugh meant the world to me.

Although I often had to interpret what Mary was feeling, I could always tell when she was happy. When her tone became more energetic and faster and the volume of her voice would get louder, they were sure signs.

But what informed me the most were her facial expressions.

In addition to smiles, her mouth told a lot, indicated by the tightness of her lips, how she was holding or rubbing her mouth, or even how quickly or methodically she was eating her fruit for evening snack. She sometimes puffed out her cheeks when she was happy, like when I started singing a familiar song to her. This seemed like she was joining in the best she could.

Her eyes also voiced a lot. Raised eyebrows, eyes wide open or faster blinking indicated excitement, alertness or playfulness, which was often accompanied by an increased speed of her singing or humming. Furrowed eyebrows or a tilted head with an unexplainable look in her eyes indicated inquisitiveness or not understanding, as if she was trying to figure something out. Eyes closed had to be taken in context with other signs, as this could be either due to tiredness or when she was in a lovey mood, indicating she was more serious or amorous than playful.

Her sweet, as opposed to broad, smile and the intensity she stared into my eyes indicated her being serious or loving. Depending on the circumstances, I could usually tell if she was telling me *"I'm glad you're here," "I'm sorry," "I love you," or "I know you love me."* I could usually discern whether it was a *"You've got to be kidding me"* versus an *"I want to understand you, I really do, but I can't,"* look. I hadn't seen the *"Leave me alone," "Settle down,"* or *"I don't feel like talking"* looks for years, thank God.

Body movements also told a lot about her overall mood and alertness. This was most evident when we were facing each other or dancing, but it was also obvious when we were sitting next to each other. Her body swayed forward and backward when she was more internalized but side-to-side when we were interactive. Her happy, more energetic mood was also revealed in other parts of her body. She often moved her hands, usually in opposite directions, with her feet slightly raised off the floor bouncing back and forth, all in synch to the rhythm of music playing or her own song she was humming, like her whole body was "talking."

Our communication was obviously not the normal verbal type that could often be accomplished over a phone anymore. It was very interactive, where we had to see each other and be next to or in front of each other, often using our hands. Showing affection and touching each other took our intimacy to a much deeper level that seemed to get even better over time now.

Our "talks" were now driven by feelings, not words. Mary and I "spoke" many emotions at times: love, sincerity, humor, joy, contentment, sadness, compassion, gratitude, hope and more. I feel we did a great job for two people who both realized neither could really comprehend what the other was saying.

During our times together, I thought about so many things I wanted to talk with her about. I found myself having one-sided conversations with her, sometimes out loud, sometimes in my head. There were times when I told her, "I'm so proud of you. Your hard work paid off." Other times, I might just think, *Man, she's so nice and beautiful.*

I sometimes told her about what was going on in my life, knowing she wouldn't understand, but never voicing my internal worries to her, in the event she might pick up on something negative.

Our physical methods of communicating were the best of all—hugging, touching…and dancing. She could still usually do a slow two-step, but at times dancing transformed more to swaying back and forth while holding hands. Oftentimes, we danced to our special tune or to the rhythm of her humming, which seemed to provide a good connection.

Since she started humming most of the time I was with her, I'm sure the continuous monotony of it could be aggravating to some. This was one of the reasons we stayed away from others while I was there. The other reason we kept to ourselves was so we could be alone, with our vocal and physical interactions uninhibited and unencumbered.

I believe Mary's humming represented the emergence of her inner self, for which she had prepared so long and hard, showing she was content. To me it showed how her years of preparation had paid off.

On a few occasions, I told Mary, "I'm writing a story about you, and it's a happy story."

She smiled, most likely due to the tone of my voice.

I asked her, "Do you know *why* it's a happy story?"

She asked with her usual response to an obvious, emphasized question, "Why?"

"Because you're happy."

She smiled and I felt my eyes tear up.

Chapter 23

The Residents

Most of the residents in assisted living and memory care don't seem to have many frequent visitors unless they have a spouse or sometimes local offspring who are able to visit regularly. I guess most people just don't have time anymore, they have too far to travel, they feel uncomfortable about it, or they battle with a combination of those issues. I've sensed that some people visit as more of a dreaded obligation.

Being one of very few daily visitors, I noticed a lot—like how some guests who entered the building passed right by residents sitting around, making no eye contact or otherwise recognizing their existence.

One time, I witnessed a female resident say hello to a visitor walking by, trying to be friendly and eagerly looking at him for some recognition, but she received no acknowledgment whatsoever. I was sitting close by. She looked at me and said, "What am I, chopped liver?"

I learned from that and similar experiences and have always tried to talk to other residents and show some interest in them, even if it was just as I walked past them. It's important for them to know they're still significant. As confused or upset as they could be at times, all of the residents seemed to be pretty nice people…and they could get very lonely.

Another time, I went out of my way to talk with a lady in a wheelchair who was sitting by herself. After a brief and superficial talk, she said, "I appreciate you coming over and speaking to me like I'm a human being and not a sack of wheat."

Most had an unusually good sense of humor. However, trying to joke with them was something I had to be careful about since something I said might be taken the wrong way or misunderstood. So I just tried to stay light-hearted and even jovial with them.

I saw many of the residents every day and tried to make sure I at least acknowledged each of them with a quick hello or wave. Calling them by name always seemed meaningful. I stopped to chat and socialize some, but I tried being careful not to let this take too much time, since any time spent with them was time I couldn't spend with Mary.

What always seemed to make their day were compliments, for almost anything. It could be noticing they had their hair done or were wearing a nice-looking outfit, shoes, purse, necklace or other jewelry. Telling them they were looking good was never met with anything other than a smile or "thank you." Asking if they had a good day or a good dinner seemed appreciated, regardless of the answer, which was usually positive. Simple acknowledgements such as these seemed to raise their level of dignity and give them a reason to smile. I especially enjoyed it when I made them laugh.

Residents seemed to especially like talking about the weather, which was an innocuous topic. This was especially a good subject when the weather was bad; there was no way they could go out, and it was interesting to them to find out what was happening in the outer world.

Many of the female residents wanted to hold my hand while I talked with them. Similarly, it was important for some of the men to have physical contact with others by shaking hands. Physical contact in a friendly way meant a lot to almost everyone. If it seemed appropriate and welcomed, I often put my hand on one of their shoulders to have contact without any intimidation.

Even residents who were more severely impaired could hear and respond some. The sound of a friendly voice, especially taking someone's hand or touching his or her shoulder, usually evoked warm smiles and meant a lot.

I noticed that if residents couldn't hear well, they became more isolated and withdrawn because they weren't able to participate in activities or conversations appropriately. I feel some of the residents would have appeared more functional and cooperative if they could hear better, and therefore understand what was happening, whether they were suffering from dementia or not.

All of the residents had at least some problem, even if it was just the ailments that come with getting older. There was a wide variety of residents in both assisted living and memory care, and mental and physical capabilities spanned the spectrum.

It's interesting that a few residents thought Mary was my mother, likely because it's usually parents who live in these facilities. Most others thought she was my daughter. Mary always looked younger than me and aged much more gracefully during this time than I did.

One night in her earlier months in assisted living I had gone in to see Mary and found her talking with someone else at the time and I didn't want to just barge in and take her away. I was very happy when she was interacting with others since I wasn't there all the time. A man and woman, both in wheelchairs, were sitting quietly near the reception desk so I introduced myself to make small talk. The lady asked, "Who did you come to visit?"

I told her, "My wife Mary. That's her over there," pointing to Mary on the other side of the lobby area.

The man, who appeared somewhat frail but seemed to perk up, asked, "She's your wife?" to which I affirmed rather proudly, "Yes, she is." He looked at her again, this time with his head down a little peering over the top of his glasses, then looked at me and stated, "That's a damn lie." I actually took it as a complement… to Mary…which made me proud of her that he thought she was so much younger.

Residents were usually nice and cooperative, although some had more difficult times as they went through different stages. There were a few residents in both areas who were occasionally somewhat loud and disruptive or complained, which mostly occurred in memory care. Sometimes they grumbled because they thought they weren't being listened to or attended to by caregivers as they thought they should be. Sometimes it was because they wanted to go to bed immediately, regardless of how early it was or if their primary caregiver was available. Sometimes it was because they thought it was morning and not evening, or vice versa. Occasionally, they forgot they had just eaten and wanted dinner.

Sometimes there were legitimate complaints about being too cold, when all a caregiver needed to do was get them a sweater or blanket. I'm sure it was a necessity in some cases for the caregivers not to cater to all the wants, whims, and complaints of demanding residents, as some could take up all of a caregiver's (or multiple caregivers') time if allowed.

Vocalizations or outbursts were not common, but did occur occasionally, and a few of these bothered me at first. Building up a tolerance to such annoyances, but more importantly, trying to understand where these people were coming from, was helpful.

From a more selfish standpoint, I became more accepting of any such outbursts or noises as I realized Mary (or me in later years) might start exhibiting such behaviors one day and would want others to be tolerant. To my knowledge, Mary had never had any outbursts. However, she did hum a lot of the time. It usually wasn't loud, but I'm sure it could be irritating to someone next to her trying to watch TV. This is another reason I kept her away from the living room in the evening, especially since she hummed more when I was with her.

Residents in memory care didn't usually interact with each other much on their own, as many didn't necessarily have the wherewithal to carry on a good two-way conversation except for pleasantries. But some were able to do this with each other, which was meaningful for them. It was nice to see and hear them carrying on a conversation with each other and enjoying it, or helping each other in some way, like putting a sweater over someone's shoulders or pushing someone in a wheelchair if allowed.

Mary liked being with some of the residents, especially in the beginning of her stay. As her illness progressed, and especially with the compounding sedation from medications, real conversations with them gradually subsided. Pleasantries with other residents were often superficial with smiles and hellos, but even though she warmed up to the staff much more, these interactions made a big difference to Mary.

A few residents specifically befriended Mary early on. This was good for her overall, as she had someone to pal around with even if there couldn't be a good two-way conversation.

Regretfully, sometimes the other person, always a female, seemed to want someone to listen while she talked about something making her unhappy at the time, usually related to wanting to go home. This certainly didn't help Mary, but she seemed to take it in stride, or likely not comprehend what all was being said. Nevertheless, she was a good listener for the others.

Alzheimer's patients can sometimes be great for each other. One lady in memory care would "jibber-jabber" (the lady's words, not mine) often talking nonsensically although with words clearly spoken. She sometimes talked to Mary in a loving, motherly manner, smiling and touching Mary's face, even giving her a little kiss on her forehead. Mary looked directly at her and listened intently, giving this lady her full attention. She gave Mary comfort and a loving acknowledgment, and Mary smiled and sometimes touched the lady's face too. They bonded and were both better for the experience. They were also happy to just sit next to each other.

At times, some residents thought Mary was mad or unfriendly if she didn't talk or respond to them—which she was unable to do at times. On occasion they became upset and said hurtful things to her, which (it seemed) Mary didn't understand, but who knows how much was absorbed.

In some respects, it was good Mary couldn't comprehend a lot of what was said. Eventually her interactions with the staff were much better than those with the other residents who had their own problems and couldn't understand "differences" others might have.

Early on, Mary had befriended Ester, a lady who was ninety years old and confined to a wheelchair. They had long talks, sometimes holding each other's hands. She had been a nun, and she and Mary prayed together some.

When Mary moved to memory care, they didn't see each other as often, although I always made sure we went over to say hello when we passed through the first-floor lobby of the assisted living facility if she was there. Mary had gained weight in the meantime, and one time Ester reached over to feel Mary's stomach and asked, "When is it due?"

There was no response or reaction from Mary, and I don't think she was able to put it together at the time, but I told Ester, "We'll see you again when we come back inside," and scurried Mary away to head outside.

Another time, while Mary was in memory care, we were walking through the main lobby of assisted living to go outside. One lady, who was unusually talkative and spoke in a loud voice, and who should have known Mary's condition, said to her "You look nice. How are you?"

Mary couldn't respond by this time.

"What's the matter? Cat got your tongue?"

With no further response from Mary, the lady felt offended and scolded my wife. "You're a bad girl."

In the early years in the residence, the woman's words would have most certainly put Mary in a down spirit. Luckily, I don't think Mary realized anything negative had been said and we went on our way. I had always talked with this lady going in to see Mary and on the way out if she was there, but I steered away from her if Mary was with me after this episode. Knowing the quirks of other residents was helpful.

For a short time in memory care, Mary occasionally walked around with her tongue sticking out a little, possibly due to her antipsychotic medications. Once, another resident, who always seemed to be prim and proper with her dress, stood with her walker in front of Mary. She looked at Mary and said, "You stick your tongue out at me…I'll stick my tongue out at you," and stuck her tongue out in a nasty way. Mary didn't react, and, again, it was impossible to know how such actions affected her, if at all. Whenever such interactions occurred, I quickly took her away, talked gently to her, and gave her extra hugs.

Sometimes residents asked me, "What's her problem?" or "What's wrong with her?" with Mary standing right there.

I wasn't about to say anything in front of Mary, so I always responded with, "We can talk about this later," and then quickly exited so no more questions or comments had a chance to surface.

Mary was never good with conflict and it was not in her nature to argue. I don't know how much of the above types of interactions she didn't comprehend versus chose to ignore. As she started walking more slowly and not talking, some seemed to stare as we passed by, which was okay since Mary didn't seem to notice.

We gradually stayed more and more to ourselves during my visits. Mary liked this, and it omitted any negative reactions with other residents, which in all fairness were rare. When we were with other residents, I always wanted to be friendly and talk with them some. However, too much of this wasn't good while I was with Mary. She usually desired my constant and undivided attention while I was there and didn't want me to pay too much attention to or spend too much time with other residents. This was understandable, but I wanted to be nice and talk with them to some extent since many of them had infrequent visitors, at least during the evening times I was there.

I tried to be considerate of other residents and didn't want them to feel uncomfortable with Mary and me showing any affection other than holding hands as we walked, which was okay since the caregivers often did this with all of them. But over time, we ended up spending much of our time in her room, or at least walking down halls or in areas where others didn't congregate, of course being friendly and talking with them when they crossed our path. Sometimes, Mary was still being taken care of in her room after dinner when I arrived, so I usually spent this time socializing with the other residents.

It was easy to be thrown for a loop by what someone said. A little over three years at the residence, I went to see Mary after work as usual, planning to take her for a drive to see some deer. She was being cared for in her room, so I took advantage of this time to visit with some of the other residents. One lady came up to me and asked, "What are you doing here?"

I told her, "I'm here to visit someone."

"Your mother?"

"No, it's my wife," which I thought was important to note, especially since she had seen Mary and me walking holding hands.

She replied, "You put her here...so you could play around and have fun?"

I told her, "No, I wouldn't do anything like that."

She then tilted her head back to have a good look at me and said, "Yeah, right!" with an all-knowing look, then walked away.

I was devastated someone would think this of me, irrespective of the fact they had cognitive issues. I had to keep up a positive spirit for Mary that evening, but this was on my mind for several days. Mary's overall status reconfirmed taking her home wouldn't work, but this statement was all it took to restart the guilt trip of whether to try it. I tried to shrug off such instances, but it was still difficult. I knew I couldn't control what residents said or did, only myself and my reaction.

This lady often asked me the same types of questions and was somewhat of a character. Another time she asked, "Who are you visiting?"

"My wife."

She thought for a moment and asked, "Do you live alone?"

"Yes."

She thought a bit more, looked at me, raised an eyebrow, and said, somewhat seductively, "We need to talk sometime."

Another lady wanted me to take her home with me, thinking we had known each other and were friends for many years and that I knew all her family. It seemed the best response was, "That would be nice, wouldn't it. I'm sorry I can't, but I'll see you here."

While I might have known what some residents needed to hear at the time and I could play along with them to make them feel better for the moment, I needed to be careful not to go against what the staff or their family members were telling them. I didn't want to raise their hopes for something that wasn't going to happen. I kept responses as general and as friendly as possible. It was often a difficult balance when they seemed to be obsessed with a thought or fear, and I couldn't provide an answer that made them happy. Sometimes the most appropriate response was, "I'm sorry, but I don't know. Or, "I'm sorry, but I can't help you with that since I don't work here."

Some residents didn't know why they were there and felt they should be home, sometimes thinking they were abandoned, regardless of the fact they had visitors. In many cases, this was due to forgetfulness or not being able to comprehend the needs of their conditions.

In a few cases, it seemed they were never told what their problem was, which I guess could make their lives even more unsettling. Caregivers can't tell anyone what their problem is, as this has to come from a doctor or family member. From my support group, I know it's difficult to tell someone they have Alzheimer's, so it's often put off or avoided altogether. One visitor told me a resident friend was upset because no one had ever told him what his problem was or why he was staying there.

Knowing some of these situations, I feel very blessed that Mary wanted to know if she had Alzheimer's so she could prepare for it and do something about it for herself while she could.

Most often, residents just wanted someone to listen to them—possibly a new set of ears—plus a little reassurance that everything was okay. When in doubt, it was always better to let the caregivers, who were trained to deal with these situations, handle a resident's worries or needs, with me "only" being friendly with them, but sometimes I helped dispel their concerns.

One man was worried and said on several occasions, "I can't find my toolbox," and was looking around for it.

I told him, "I'll look for it and let you know when I find it, so you don't need to worry about it." Another time, I told him, "Your toolbox is right where it's supposed to be."

Each time he said, "Thank you very much," and quit worrying.

Often, my telling them I'd check into it—whatever their problem or complaint was at the time—was all it took for them to quit fretting over it. Or if they said they were waiting for or looking for someone, my telling them, "If I see them, I'll let them know you're looking for them," went a long way.

A few residents were often worried in the evening, stating they needed to leave to go home or to a relative's house. They thought they needed to leave but couldn't find a way out. What I found worked best was to tell them, "It's getting dark outside (and it's cold, if appropriate). Why don't you stay here tonight and think about leaving in the morning?"

A common response was, "But I don't have any place to stay tonight."

"Yes, you do. They have a room for you here, and it's a very nice room."

This seemed to always take care of their immediate concerns about leaving so they could settle down for the evening.

While there were some minor issues from time to time, Mary and the other residents at least cohabitated well. I believe this is where all of Mary's years of preparation paid off for her and all those around her. She had a loving heart she had worked to fill with good thoughts ahead of time.

Dealing with residents daily provided me with a new appreciation for these people and benefitted me too. My experiences highlighted the ignorance and insensitivity of how I approached such situations previously and hopefully helped me grow a little kinder and more compassionate as a result.

Honestly, I often didn't want to deal with the same unsolvable problems again and again, getting drawn into their world. Some would take up my whole time if I let them. However, there was always the nagging thought, *what if our circumstances were reversed, and that was me?* So, within reason, I talked with them and tried to dispel their worries until the next day, but Mary still had to come first.

Chapter 24

Angels and Miracles

What made our situation work for us and a primary factor in Mary being happy were the residence facility's caregivers and staff—the "unsung heroes" or "angels of care."

Visiting Mary virtually every day, I acquired a good feel for what takes place in both assisted living and memory care where she lived and the nature of caregivers in general.

My sense is that being a caregiver is not "just a job" to most of these people, but it's a real "profession" or even a "labor of love." I know, like everyone else, these people need their jobs to earn a living. But I've talked with many who said they do what they do in large part for their love of people and wanting to help those in need, in some cases to honor God, and as much more than a job to make money. I truly believe we could all learn lessons in humanity and humility from these people.

The caregivers at Meadowside generally were each responsible for certain residents on a given day, but they also seemed to have a real team spirit, helping each other as needed. For example, as I was leaving one evening, I asked one of the caregivers if she was taking care of Mary, and I was told a different caregiver had her that evening. I needed to leave shortly and didn't see her caregiver and informed the person it seemed Mary needed changing, with the intent of her informing the one in charge of Mary. The person I spoke with went directly over to Mary to take care of her.

There was a policy at the facility that gifts could not be given to individual caregivers. While there were some who took care of Mary more often or paid her special attention during certain stages, this type of teamwork with all involved made this a good policy. But I would have loved to give presents to many of them.

Caregivers had breaks scheduled at specific times so there was always an appropriate number of staff available to take care of the residents. Other than their breaks it seemed that they could rarely truly rest, always needing to be vigilant since anything could happen at any time with Alzheimer's patients.

Most residents were friendly and cooperative overall and seemed to appreciate what was being done for them. However, some refused help (sometimes physically) or were verbally abusive at times. The caregivers always seemed to take it in stride and realized the residents often didn't have control over what they did or said. I don't think I would have the patience or fortitude to do it!

It's human nature to want to be nicer to those who are nice to you, but the staff at Meadowside always seemed to take the decreased cognitive and physical abilities of all of the residents into consideration, showing civility and respect no matter what, whether their efforts were recognized or rejected.

Yet there seemed to be times when the caregivers needed to draw boundaries with some residents who would take their constant attention if allowed. These times seemed most prevalent when residents were obsessed about needing to go home or were continually asking for help when there was nothing with which they needed aid. Regardless, caregivers spent a lot of time consoling such residents.

Everyone is different, and some caregivers were better than others interacting with residents. I'm sure all caregivers have had days they weren't totally "up for it" or would rather be somewhere else. I'm certain there were times each of the caregivers had a "bad day," as everyone has from time to time, but they rarely, if ever, seemed to show it.

There were a few caregivers in particular with whom Mary developed stronger bonds. These were the ones who seemed to spend a little more time with her, talking to her more normally even when she couldn't respond, presenting a gentle and unhurried demeanor when taking care of her. In earlier years, Mary especially appreciated the time they spent putting makeup on her.

Mary often stood next to these extra loving caregivers to be close and sometimes followed them around because she wanted to be with them. This was likely annoying or inconvenient for them at times, but they were good about it and made her feel a part of whatever was happening.

All of the staff members at least acknowledged her by saying "Hi Mary" as they passed by, often stopping to briefly talk or give her a hug during stages she needed it the most. I also tried to interact with the caregivers while I was with Mary, at least subconsciously showing her we all were her "family."

In fact, over time they were more of a family to Mary on a day-to-day, moment-to-moment basis than I was. But they also became family to me. I always asked them to call me by Marc and not "Mr. Alderdice."

Periodically, the facility had special events like live musical performances or special holiday parties. There were celebrations for official holidays, as well as ones such as St. Patrick's Day,

Mardi Gras, or the facility's anniversary. The residence was decorated, and residents were dressed with party hats, necklaces, flowers, or whatever was appropriate for the occasion. And, of course, there were refreshments and music.

The parties were great, but it was the staff that made them special. The staff were active and cheerful, and they were even great dancers!

Usually the staff danced with residents who could stand or even danced while holding hands with someone in a wheelchair. Once I saw one of the caregivers holding hands with a resident and dancing while another staff member held the person up from the back.

I was meeting with some folks from church one time. They asked how Mary was doing. I told them she was doing well overall and, most importantly, she was happy, and I couldn't ask for anything better under the circumstances. We talked about different kinds of miracles, and one of the people prayed that angels would watch over Mary. At that moment, I realized my prayers had been answered.

Short of a truly phenomenal miracle (like reversing the disease, with Mary returning back to her normal self), I had been praying all along for Mary to be happy...and now she was. I know my being with her every day added to that, but I knew she needed more—much more than I could give her.

I realized at that point that Meadowside's caregivers were like angels to Mary. Whether they were provided by God, or were simply truly good people who wanted to help others, didn't make any difference. One way or another they were a true miracle for Mary...and me.

Chapter 25

A Renewed Love Affair

A very special time for us began three to four years after Mary moved into memory care and she had settled in and had been taken off all major psychotropic medications for at least a year.

As sad as the overall situation was, we almost always had great visits. Our times together at this stage were almost like two people who had recently fallen in love, getting to know each other and wanting to be "in touch" with the other. Even small tangibles, like running my fingers through her hair or rubbing her arms, meant a lot to her. We did a good bit of simple teasing and silly things, and we both laughed a lot. She was happy to see me, and I looked forward to being with her and stayed as long as I reasonably could.

She had great stamina for standing or walking and generally preferred to stand than sit, so we walked a lot. There was a credenza at the end of a hallway. Part of it couldn't be seen from down the hall since it extended into an offshoot hallway. Sometimes as we meandered down, I leaned against it with Mary in front of me. This was a bit awkward since our faces were far apart because of my height, so I started sitting on the credenza with legs apart so Mary could lean against me in between my legs, up against the credenza. This worked great because she could stand, I could sit, we were close to each other, and our faces were at the same height. Plus, we couldn't be seen from down the hall, but I could see if someone was coming not too far away. There we could hold each other, sing, or just be silly—without embarrassing anyone since we never wanted to do that.

Mary prized this because it was easy to touch faces. She especially liked laying her chin in my cupped hands or my stroking her cheek. Just our leaning forward and touching heads, whether forehead-to-forehead or cheek-to-cheek, was special.

The credenza worked great for a while, until one of the newer residents snuck up on us one evening. Our heads weren't touching, but Mary had her hands on my neck, and she was singing. The resident looked at us and said indignantly, "Making love in the hallway! You should be ashamed of yourselves." While we were doing nothing resembling "making love," I certainly didn't want to make anyone feel uncomfortable, so I decided to devise an option.

I brought in a bar stool from home and kept it in her room. I sat on the stool, Mary stood in front of me, and we could "make love" as much as we wanted in the privacy of her room. Of course, we never did anything we would be embarrassed about if someone entered the room, and sometimes they did, but this was likely the closest thing to "making out" that could be done with a more advanced Alzheimer's patient in a residential facility. We both relished it.

In the privacy of her room we could express our feelings in both words and actions, which seemed to mean more and more to her, and this way no one else would feel embarrassed, uneasy, or sad in the case of those who had lost a close loved one or perhaps never had anyone special.

The staff were tolerant with Mary and me, but I tried to make sure we only held hands in public and I only touched her face with my hand when I left. Any other affections were best done in private, not solely for the sake of others, but for Mary's so we weren't inhibited.

She needed an over-expression of physical contact at this stage, especially with her lack of verbal comprehension. She still had a lot of love to give, and the desire and capacity to accept it. She needed love and affection and vocalization, whether through actual words or humming.

We had our "sessions" for long times, with Mary standing and me sitting on the stool. I didn't have much padding to sit on, so sometimes it became uncomfortable and my legs would become numb and I would need to move on while I could still walk. Usually by then it was snack time which I now always stayed for, but also close to the time I needed to leave anyway to take care of Cody since he had been alone and not been let out since I left for work in the morning.

Mary never stopped these sessions on her own and sometimes I felt bad having to stop them, so one time I made the decision to continue as long as she wanted. This worked great—for about forty-five minutes, at which time her eyes rolled back, and she passed out due to standing so long in one place without moving. This was frightening at first but, in retrospect I remembered that this happens to military personnel who lock their legs while standing at attention too long. *Why didn't I think of that?*

I lowered her to the floor slowly and she regained consciousness within a few seconds. A caregiver entered the room shortly after this happened while Mary was still on the floor. We checked her out, let her lie on the floor until she seemed her normal self, and helped her up. She was fine with no further problems that day, but I did change our routine. While our sessions might add up to a lengthy period, we engaged in them in spurts, no longer than fifteen to twenty minutes at a time, taking breaks with some walking in between.

Though taking breaks was necessary for her safety and my bottom, they interrupted the romantic moment and so weren't best for her emotionally. During our initial session, she was often exuberantly happy and romantic. After our breaks, she lost her high-spirited mood, and we never quite returned to the initial level of intimacy. Still I couldn't take the chance of her passing out so we made the best of it.

Another time I noticed her eyes starting to roll back and I lowered her to the floor, but I know she didn't pass out all the way because she kept humming the whole time, never missing a beat or slowing down her rhythm. After that episode, I started putting a chair behind her, since there was no way I could help her up off the floor by myself. This allowed us to continue a little longer, and there were a few times she needed a place to sit quickly.

She "came alive" during our face-to-face sessions, which created a totally different mood than holding hands while sitting or walking. Her face was radiant as she smiled or laughed. It was like we bypassed the part of her brain affected by Alzheimer's and directly stimulated the center of her brain that controlled emotions. We reached her inner passions, way beyond her verbal comprehension. There was nothing sexual about it, but it was highly emotionally sensual and passionate.

We had great "conversations." I usually couldn't understand what she was trying to say, but it rarely mattered. It was all pleasant, even if meaningless, talk. She often did her "rhythm talking," where she sang a song with or without words. The words usually didn't make any sense, but she almost always wore a loving smile. Often it seemed her singing was directed to me during these times, since she usually looked straight into my eyes or rubbed her cheek against mine or played with my face. Her vocalizations, which weren't actual words, were melodious, and she often gradually changed the sounds to others that rhymed without ever changing the rhythm. Sometimes she transitioned from singing to humming, which was easier for her, yet expressed the same sentiments.

Occasionally she was deeply passionate with overly expressive intonations while singing to me in a loving and romantic tone. She often smiled like in the old days when she was singing and signing the worship songs at church, totally engrossed in her feelings. Sometimes she was more active and playful, gently grabbing my nose and smiling, as a bit of a tease.

Mary often looked into my eyes, usually penetratingly deeply, and told me she loved me. Even if she didn't say it, I could tell that was what she felt. By looking at Mary's expressions and how she was interacting with me physically, there's no doubt in my mind she was telling me, "*I love you. I know you love me. Thank you.*" A couple of times she said, "You're my heart," while gazing into my eyes. Early on she tried to remove my glasses to have more direct eye contact, so I started not wearing them when I visited.

I looked directly into her eyes in response, to a depth I had never accomplished before. It was more like we were talking with our eyes at a primal level to replace the inabilities for verbal communication. It seemed she wanted to see my inner thoughts and feelings. For the first time, I'm almost embarrassed to say, I really focused on the character and color of her eyes—hazel that sometimes seemed to change color depending on the light or surroundings, from fern green to radiant golden, with a thin pewter grey rim around the edge.

I tried to make sure I gazed directly into her eyes, so she knew we were connected. However, what I wanted most was for her to be happy, and so I loved looking at her smiles which showed me everything. I caught myself looking at her smiles more than her eyes. When she smiled, I knew it was a real smile and she was content. She had progressed beyond the point of being able to fake emotions, much less a smile, simply to be nice. I knew she was truly happy—and that made me incredibly contented under the circumstances. We simply loved each other and seized the moment for all it was worth, sharing a true connection in spirit.

She gave me her undivided devotion during these sessions, and she needed my constant attention while I was with her. I seemed to captivate her, and it thrilled me to know she wanted me and needed me even now.

I sometimes became lost in the moment—and for just a few seconds, it was like I was in a time machine, back to where we were before this awful disease called Alzheimer's took root. My head might be against her cheek or neck, she was singing, and it was easy to drift off, subconsciously pretending everything was like it was years before. It was nice to savor these moments… but I couldn't allow myself to become too wrapped up in it or distracted from the present for Mary's safety. Being "zoned out" a bit made the time go by quickly. It was similar to driving a car almost automatically, then realizing you weren't consciously thinking about driving and were further along than you thought.

Having these "therapy" sessions—in an appropriate setting of course—was good for Mary and me, and we both looked forward to them. It was like we were in our own little world, an escape from the reality of our situation for a little while. It was truly a marvelous time and meant a lot to me.

Mary was extremely happy, especially at times we were "making love." It seemed like she experienced an endorphin high she would not have attained with normal talking and interactions. I know I helped her reach this emotional level where she could truly enjoy the moment and be happy.

Our love for each other, and showing it, was how I could "reach" her and connect and communicate with her despite the fact she couldn't coherently speak anymore and became mostly nonverbal. It opened up a two-way street, strengthened our bond, helped me become sane and whole again.

It would have been terrible for her (and me) if we had to depend only on verbal interaction to make her happy. These feelings were directly from the heart, without having to deal with verbal attempts that can often lead to misstatements or misunderstanding of words.

The physical contact was a great emotional morale booster for both of us too. She had a loving spirit and she loved me. She lifted my spirits when I was down. I felt better after being with her, regardless of how my workday had gone or how much I needed to do once I got home. I may have looked serious or contemplative when she wasn't looking because I sometimes drifted off to think about other things on my mind, but I always felt myself smile once her attention drew back to me.

Shortly after we started walking around following these sessions, Mary's demeanor started to change. I didn't know whether she knew our walk meant I was going to leave soon afterwards, or the emotions part of her brain was no longer activated when our closeness and intimacy was broken, or she started to go "down" for the evening.

I didn't want her to connect our stopping with my departure for the evening so I started staying for a longer time after we tapered our "love" sessions. This provided a good wind-down time together. It was great when we left on a positive note, both verbally and mentally happy, especially at times she acknowledged we would see each other again tomorrow.

As a bonus, these times helped to lift the guilt I had for so long about not being able to bring her back home to live. Funny how it turned out—Mary, the one with the problems and the one who needed all the help, once again ended up being my salvation for sanity.

Our second love affair was certainly different from our first one that had lasted so many years. Now, we accepted each other exactly as we were with no other expectations. We were just happy to be with each other.

Outside each resident's door was a glass frame that could be personalized. A number of these had different quotes, whether put there by a resident's family or the staff. One by Vivian Greene seemed particularly relevant to our situation:

"Life isn't about waiting for the storm to pass, it's about learning to dance in the rain."

In our case, the storm didn't pass us by, so we danced in a number of ways for as long as we could, whenever we could. Our new "love affair" allowed us to do this.

Mary was extremely happy during the period of our renewed love affair. Each day was a good day with people she loved, and our times together were special.

My approach to ensuring Mary's happiness was reminiscent of *Groundhog Day*, the film in which Bill Murray started a particular day over and over, with him being the only one remembering what happened during the previous day. Initially, he felt sorry for himself, living in the same rut day after day. He often did rotten things to people because he knew he could get away with it, and the next morning he could start over without anyone knowing what he had done. After numerous blunders, he decided to make the most of each new day by trying to better himself, learning new skills and more importantly, how to better interact with people and make them happy. He experimented, found out what did or did not work, and applied it the next day, with the intention of each day being better than the previous one. He eventually achieved the perfect day where he wowed and wooed Andie MacDowell, his coworker he was trying to impress, and they fell in love.

I essentially had the same opportunity with Mary each day. Like in *Groundhog Day*, I strived to learn from my mistakes and tried to make each day better than the previous one for her, if not her best day ever. And the happier she was, the happier I was.

I was able to use what I had learned over many days and now years regarding what worked well, or didn't work so well, to build and nurture a foundation within Mary. Doing so, the feelings not only carried over to the next day, but became exponential, getting better even if she didn't remember the specifics. It's hard to know what Mary remembered from day to day, but the lingering good feelings obviously carried forward to the next day and made her life happier in general over time.

A lot of what I did was by trial and error, and I wasn't afraid to try something different. If it worked—great, I'd do it again and try to improve on it. If it didn't work—also good, since now I knew what to avoid. It was unlikely she would remember it the next day so almost anything was worth a try. What didn't work well one time was sometimes effective on a different occasion, so it never hurt to re-try an approach since a difference in her moods and reception sometimes occurred.

The present was paramount. Mary only knew *now*. She didn't remember the bad times but luckily the good times seemed to have a cumulative effect on her soul.

I always wanted to leave on a good note. Her last impression of me was all she would likely remember, or have lingering feelings about until the next day, so I wanted to make each day special.

While I certainly don't want to sound morbid, from a somewhat selfish standpoint, knowing how guilt and regrets burden me, to be honest I also wanted to feel good about each visit, knowing it could always be the last one.

I was thankful Mary didn't remember the bad times and was now happy with me, with herself, and with her surroundings. She knew me on an intimate level, loved me, and enjoyed being with me. She was happy day by day, and each day was a new day, a do-over day, and I strived to make every day her best day ever.

Chapter 26

Present Day

At the time of this writing, Mary was diagnosed with Alzheimer's over ten years ago and has lived in the same residence facility for close to eight years. She has no significant medical problems but is slowing down physically. She walks slowly with assistance and never gets out of a chair on her own. She's been off all major psychiatric medications for five years and has also been in an overall good mental, emotional and, I feel sure, spiritual state during this time.

Our daily routine hasn't changed much over the last couple of years. She still hums to herself—or others interacting with her—much of the time. She's now always sitting quietly when I arrive, often with her head down resting against her right hand. But she hums most of the time I'm with her, still attempting to talk at times, once I help her up and we're away from the others. She still seems to turn into a different person when we're at a place where I feel comfortable having our one-on-one interactions. For Mary, our alone time is definitely needed and cherished far more than staying with the others to watch TV, which she rarely does any longer.

I took another short trip to Colorado last year, again worrying about whether it would make much difference to Mary. Upon returning, she smiled at me right away and started to hum as soon as I sat next to her. After this trip, she seemed clingier, generally holding onto me tighter overall or locking her fingers through one of my beltloops, which was fine with me. I had missed her too.

Since Mary and I still want and need a lot of closeness with uninhibited time away from others, the residence placed a "loveseat" or padded bench in the shared room of her suite. This provides the perfect place for us to sit next to each other in private, but we still do as much walking around as she's up for, since I want to keep her as fit and mobile as possible. I usually walk backwards holding both her hands, which is not only more personal facing each other but allows us to walk a little faster.

We're still happy to be with each other. Every day is nice with happy "talk" and good vibes. We still have our "intimate" times with hugs and humming. I'm not sure who needs it more. She's in a contented place emotionally and physically, and so am I when I'm with her.

It's difficult for me to state objectively how much or how rapidly Mary has declined because I see her every day. Over these years she's gone through various stages and had many good days. I understand that fluctuations in behavior and even wide mood swings are not uncommon with Alzheimer's, but Mary didn't seem to have many once she finally settled down.

She's generally become less responsive with less expressiveness in her face and voice. Her ups and downs haven't been numerous or large, but I've usually tried to read too much into them—so my life can still be a roller coaster ride at times. I was not psychologically prepared for a recent milestone we reached—when a wheelchair was ordered for her. She became unsteady in the mornings after getting out of bed and in the late evening and this was needed for her safety. While appreciated, I've rarely used it and always walk a lot with her.

She's much more loving and interactive when we're alone, but that's likely because I am. I doubt it would make any difference to her whether we were in a crowd or it's just us. She seems to lean on me more and enjoy putting her head on my shoulder or pushing her head into my cheek for more intimate contact. Sometimes she puts her hand on my head or around my neck, looking at me tenderly, as if she's saying "It's okay. You'll be okay," seemingly comforting me instead of me consoling her.

While the intense feelings of our peak "love affair" have faded, she's still very cuddly and affectionate. She still comes alive as we walk off together, with happiness and warmth in her eyes.

She never complains, which I'm sure means she's content. However, I'm not sure how she would let anyone know if she was sick or in pain.

I've never wanted to leave her when she was in a good mood, happy, more active, or affectionate. Now, she's always in that emotional state. I believe she's currently in the frame of mind she was working towards as she was preparing her heart and spirit before the diagnosis—contented emotionally, pleasant to others, and happy for what she has.

It's difficult to know how much of her good state is due to her preparation, my daily involvement, caregivers, or disease variations—although I would guess it's probably all of these. While it's likely a stretch to say Mary enjoys life, I do believe with all my heart that she's still able to be happy.

There have been times in these later years when she started to say something that seemed to make sense as a serious statement, like she realized what was going on, but soon started to hum and the thought was gone. Sometimes, she shows a perplexed, questioning look that quickly dissipates to humming.

"Our tune" that we had made up shortly after she moved to assisted living has become too complicated for her, though she'll try to hum along some if I start it. But she's now happy with her own melodies, which have become very simplified tunes over time. She sometimes hums her tunes while sitting in a chair by herself, but mostly it's the times she's one-on-one with someone.

It's impossible to know what she's feeling or thinking for sure, but I choose to try to have a positive outlook on it all. Understanding her when she tries to talk now is impossible, except for lovey words or phrases. While I usually don't know what she's trying to say, I still respond, and we continue to have good "conversations."

It's not uncommon for Alzheimer's patients to be more lucid on some days, and I'm amazed when she's said very unexpected but great words. The following quotes are what Mary said during the period of one to two years ago.

Once she gazed deeply into my eyes and said, "You're the best, best guy in the whole..." and suddenly started humming. I understood and appreciated the message!

I spent New Year's Eve at Jeff's house, so I visited Mary before her dinner. I wasn't usually expected before dinner, so one of the caregivers wanted to check her and change her if necessary. The caregiver told me Mary was singing, "He's here, he's here," in a happy voice while getting ready. What a great way to begin a new year!

Caregivers told me one time she was singing, "Marc is coming...Marc is coming..." while getting her ready. I hadn't heard my name in a long time. At least once, she also told them, "I love him," or asked, "Where's Marc?" while getting ready for my arrival.

The director of memory care sometimes interacted with Mary more intensively on a one-to-one basis. After one of these sessions, Mary walked slowly over to the director. As she approached, she puffed out her cheeks some, then gave the director a real kiss on the cheek, looked her in her eyes and summed it up by saying one simple word, "Love."

Once she asked me, "Do you love me?"

I was surprised but quickly responded, "Yes, I love you lots. Do you love me?"

"Yes, I do," she said with a smile and little laugh.

Another time, after finishing her juice and snack, we were walking around. She was more vocal and energetic than usual. I mentioned I needed to leave soon and would come back tomorrow. She mentioned "home" in an isolated manner, followed by, "I stay here."

I responded, "This is a nice place, isn't it?"

She replied clearly, "Yes, I like it. I love it." She broke into a big smile, with a little laugh. She followed with, "Thank you so much." I was flabbergasted with the articulation and apparent understanding she expressed. This type of clarity was certainly not normal for her, but it was phenomenal…and exactly what I needed to hear.

Not too long after that, out of the blue she stated, "I'm home."

I replied, "This is a nice home."

"Yes, it is. Thank you."

The above quotes are snippets of thoughts with few words, but they are very meaningful to me and I cherish them. Whether she accepts it or is oblivious to her condition doesn't really matter—she's happy.

As part of Mary's food program, at the beginning of all meetings and sponsor calls, they recited the Serenity Prayer:

God grant me the serenity
to accept the things I cannot change,
the courage to change the things I can,
and the wisdom to know the difference.

This "Twelve Step Prayer" helped Mary through many struggles and challenges over the years, and she must have internalized it as part of her preparation. It seems that she's accepted the things she cannot change, which has given her the serenity many patients with Alzheimer's can't seem to grasp.

In presenting Mary's story, I realize how easy it is to idealize someone or some overall situation, as if through the proverbial rose-colored glasses or perhaps selective memory. As within every marriage, ours wasn't perfect, and we've had our great times and not-so-great moments. I wish I had appreciated, if not treasured, our marriage and her more throughout.

In my interactions with Mary, I know I sometimes give her too much credit—sometimes too little—regarding how much she realizes. With her being basically nonverbal, it's difficult to tell what she's thinking or wanting to say. I've learned that when she doesn't react in a usual or expected way, it doesn't necessarily mean she's not comprehending what's going on to some degree.

Our journey with Alzheimer's has had its ups and downs, with some great times and some horrific times. Today, Mary considers the residence her home and likes it, enjoys her days, loves the staff, and, as well as she can realize it, knows this is where she needs to be. She is always happy to see me and is okay when I need to leave.

During some stages, I almost dreaded going to see her since I didn't know what her mood or reaction might be. Now, I really look forward to the visits. I still visit her every day, directly from work if it's a workday, unless there's a legitimate reason I can't. I'm beyond "normal" retirement age but continue to work full-time. Not only do I want to make sure money is available for Mary's current and future care but going to work provides a distraction and a bit of sanity for me in being around others.

I enjoy being with her, it makes both of us happy, and we leave each other better off each day. I'm able to stay with her longer than before because Cody is in true "doggie heaven," now living on three acres in West Virginia with six kids, two cats, and another dog.

How much she realizes now is hard to tell. Rarely, she still may say something like, "I'm sorry," or mention home. Throughout the years, Mary's possible realization of her plight was one of the most distressing times for me, and obviously for her. I've told her numerous times, "There's nothing for you to feel sorry about, I love you very much, I'll take care of you, and I will always be with you." I have also often told her, "I've got your back." I feel she knows all this emotionally and feels it physically, but I know the repetitive enforcement helps.

Who knows what the future will bring, but for the time being, both Mary and I are doing well and are "happy." We dance a lot—she never forgot how to dance. We "talk" and laugh together. I tease her, and she sometimes teases me back. Her general ability to react and interact has continued to decrease, but she understands love and kindness.

For her to be in the content, even happy, state she's in at this time in our journey has taken a lot of commitment from both of us. Mary put in her time as she prepared in the event she developed the disease, and then made the most of life after her diagnosis until her crazy bout of psychotic illness mysteriously appeared—and then thankfully disappeared. I've put in my time after her diagnosis to ensure she was as happy as possible. Based on her current status, our labors seemed to have worked and were well worth the time and efforts. I have no other way to explain how well she's doing...everything considered.

I've thought about it periodically, but it's mostly dawned on me over the last few years that all of her training and preparation really did pay off. The more I'm with her, the more I admire her for how she prepared herself and for how she handles herself now. Whether or not she's aware of it, her life now is just like she planned it to be if the Alzheimer's fate she feared became a reality. She filled herself with love and nice thoughts, so these traits were the ones to express themselves once she had little or no control. While I admired her during the time she was preparing herself for the possibility of coping with Alzheimer's, I'm in total awe of her now because it actually worked. She has a loving spirit about her.

Mary had a dogged determination when it came to proving to herself, if no one else, that she could do something she had never been able to do before, whether water skiing, walking on logs, losing weight—or even dealing with the devastating diagnosis and reality of early-onset Alzheimer's. She never gave up until she succeeded.

I've seen firsthand how Alzheimer's often strips away someone's best self or the person he or she used to be. I believe for Mary, it has brought out her true loving, caring, sweet, gentle, kind personality.

It may seem selfish to some for me to say this, but I hope I don't die first. I want to be there for Mary to try to make her as happy as possible for as long as possible. I know I make a difference in her life.

It's been a while since I've taken her out for just a drive, but I still take her to our house for dinner, which requires assistance. She deeply enjoyed nature before, like butterflies and sunsets and deer, and she had her "happy cries." She now hardly looks at such scenes as I point them out. But she's happy with her humming and being with me or others she loves in her own limited world. There's nothing logical about having such an inner peace under such circumstances.

On nice days, we still sometimes sit in an area in front of the residence with comfortable outdoor furniture in the midst of shade trees and flowers. There's often a beautiful blue sky with white wispy clouds and sunbeams shining through the trees lighting up the gazebo through the lattice work. I sit back and relax, something that's difficult to do at times, with my eyes closed, holding Mary's hand, feeling the nice breeze blowing. I let my mind drift to imagine we're camping again, sitting under the trees by a lake with the wind in our faces just enjoying each other. It's a nice break.

At least for Mary, I believe love will be one of the last feelings to go—or let go of—because it is the one true feeling that can't help emanating from her heart and soul. She still comes alive during our "love sessions." She usually can't *say* love and who knows if she can *think* love, but she can still *feel* love. It's a different situation, and a strange comparison, but I think I may appreciate her as a total person now more than I ever did before.

The simple things keep me going, especially her smiles and sweetness towards me. I look forward to being with her and making both of us happy. She's my main social life.

When she is doing well, it most assuredly rubs off on me. I feel heathier and happier, and I concentrate better at work, sleep better, and approach life more positively overall. The good feelings and vibes between us are catching. It's definitely a two-way street!

Over the years of our marriage Mary often told me, "It's nice when you're married to your best friend." I've always felt the same way. There's still a magnet on the fridge in our kitchen that bears this saying.

To this day, I often skip much of the worship service when I attend church, because I still visualize her standing next to me singing and signing, lost in the moment with a loving smile. It brings back good memories, but it's also sad. This also makes me miss her "I love you" sign that I haven't seen for many years now.

In the early days of Mary's disease, in my prayers I often asked for an extraordinary miracle. In the most difficult times, I just asked that God get us through. Then I switched over to asking that Mary be content and as happy as possible. I feel these later prayers have been answered.

It's easy to make wishes earlier in life about not wanting to live under certain conditions—whether cancer or Alzheimer's or other terrible diseases—but wishes, which become prayers, can change as "life happens." During the time when Mary and I were in the midst of our renewed love affair, I was walking in to visit her and a male resident asked me, "What's your wife's problem?"

I told him, "She has Alzheimer's disease."

To which he raised his eyes and replied, "Humpf, that's worse than death."

I didn't say a word but realized how much I disagreed with him.

Mary was happy—much happier than he was—albeit not in the way most people define it. Yes, there will come a time for everyone when death is inevitable, and possibly even desired, but as Mary has shown, a meaningful, loving and happy life can be lived for a long time—despite seemingly insurmountable odds—with the right mindset and preparation.

There undoubtedly have been books written and philosophical discussions throughout the ages on whether people facing circumstances such as Alzheimer's disease can truly be happy. I can attest that they can be whether they understand the full depth of their situations or not. In fact, only realizing their limited world might lead them to experience a higher plain of happiness, relatively speaking, than someone living in the real world could ever achieve because of all the "noise"—the distractions, details, and stresses "normal" life brings. Possibly having the problems of dementia when one has dementia is a blessing.

As of now, our future is unknown. Our journey has had many curves, cliffs, valleys and mountains to traverse that weren't on our original roadmap...to get to where we are today. At this point in time it's like we're in the eye of a hurricane; the violent storm has passed and inevitably another is on its way. But for now, though I feel the breeze starting to blow, it's still pleasant and calm, and we make the most of it.

Author's Note

No two stories are the same—for either those with Alzheimer's or their caregivers and loved ones, especially when the individuals affected are joined into one collective journey. Yet, while Mary's story is unique, it's similar in a lot of ways to the paths of many others. My thoughts have been from a spouse's view of our sojourn in particular, but hopefully they will be relevant and helpful for other spouses, partners, offspring, or loved ones of those who have Alzheimer's or similar maladies, as well as those who assist with their needs. There's a lot of overlap in what happens to most Alzheimer's victims at some stage or another.

Mary and I felt we were much luckier than many people. We knew or heard of some, often much younger than us, who experienced horrible events in their lives that affected them and their families significantly. Maybe being aware of such possibilities made us love and appreciate each other all the more, and we were thus able to treasure our transient lives together more than we would have otherwise. Even with this devastating disease, I feel fortunate. Since we discussed this early on I know Mary feels blessed also.

I love her. I wish more than anything our situation was better, but I'm happy I can be there for her and with her, and make sure she's being well taken care of, just as I know she would take great care of me if our roles were reversed.

Everyone knows I would be lying if I said there were not times I've felt despondent over our situation and the fact that Mary and I won't have a "normal" remainder of our lives growing old together. It was easy to allow myself to become depressed occasionally, especially when I would stop and look at what lay ahead. But if I dwelled on my worries, doubts and self-pity, I'd likely be digging my own early grave—plus I wouldn't be able to lift Mary's spirits, not to mention the fact that no one wants to be around a negative person and I still have to live life around other people. I'm grateful for what I've had and what I have, and for Mary's current happy status, which I hope will continue.

When I have felt discouraged, it's often been helpful to try to look at life from a different angle, kind of like looking in the rearview mirror as opposed to through the windshield. Instead of totally focusing on the future and its uncertainties, I like reflecting on the past, being grateful for the good life we have had together and how truly blessed our lives have been, and still are, in so many ways.

I created a "Blessings List" writing down everything—both major and minor aspects of my life, tangible and intangible—for which I am thankful. Especially during periods when I'm feeling discouraged about our situation, I review the list, and sometimes revise it, to remind myself how much I have for which to be grateful.

Some of the blessings are from the past. We have two great sons of whom we're very proud. Mary and I have been happy together for many years, shared many good times, seen a lot of places, gone on a lot of adventures, and experienced a good life together overall. We were never in any real financial stress, and I've always been fortunate to be employed so we weren't.

Some of the blessings are in the present. Mary is happy, well taken care of, healthy overall, likes where she lives, and loves the staff.

She "knows" me and is happy to be with me. Our sons have families of their own and are doing well, and we now have a grandson and a granddaughter. I still have a good job I like overall. We have some money saved, although I still need to plan and be careful with the uncertainties ahead. I fully realize our situation could always be worse in a number of ways. We're doing quite well under the circumstances, and at this point, I couldn't expect anything more.

Some of the blessings I feel when I look to the future. We only get one chance at life, and we need to make the most of it and not dwell on what might have been. I've accepted it, but certainly don't like all of it. I learned from Mary that preparation pays off, and one can have a good and even happy life in the face of adversity. We all need to make the years we have left count. Even though Mary's years left, or even mine, may be but a few, I see a happy and bright future ahead.

I encourage you to make a Blessings List or Gratitude List and refer to and update it on a regular basis, especially when your spirits are low.

A sobering wake-up call recently caught me off guard. As I was finishing this book, I asked Jeff for clarification on how he saw me dealing with my issues back when he recommended I talk with a therapist during Mary's earlier Meadowside years. I asked him this with the sole purpose of ensuring accuracy for the book. We discussed again all of the stresses at the time—how I was consumed with one pressure or another, over-committed, took no time for myself, and tried to have control over everything— whether controllable or not—in Mary's life and in mine.

After we finished going through the list of all my issues way back then, he added, "Nothing's changed...except now you don't have Cody on top of everything else." I was initially stunned, shortly planning my defense.

As we discussed it more, I thought about what had really changed (or not) from then to now. I was still obsessed about Mary and putting her above everything else in my life—still focused solely on her present happiness; I still visited her every day; I still worked too much to make sure there's plenty of money to continue taking care of her; I still honored her preparation efforts by constantly working on and finishing this book to make sure her life could make a difference in other peoples' lives, which she would have liked. All of these things have taken priority for the past seven-plus years of my life and there was still no break in my routine. Virtually my whole life has been and still is consumed with Mary. Obviously, my primary goal has been to make my wife as happy as possible from day to day, and I feel deeply satisfied with that success since my accomplishments in being a problem-solver and a "doer" make me thrive.

But my talk with Jeff made me realize once again that focusing all of my efforts toward one goal hasn't been entirely healthy.

Whether or not my priorities have been focused appropriately—then or now—I know they weren't always well balanced. *After all, how many priorities can one person have?* It's good to have priorities, but that's all they are…they are not absolutes, and they should be flexible in most cases…balanced so as not to be at the exclusion of everything else.

My attitude and approach weren't just detrimental to me early on; this imbalance has continued and even mounted to affect my life and relationships more recently. I admit I have not made enough time for friends I have been able to keep. There are a number of people in my life I would call "friends," but there's a difference in these people and the really deep friendships that can only develop by being together over many years. Obligations continue forever, but some things you can't put off or afford to lose as they're hard to gain back.

In all honesty, I'm not really sure what I would have done differently, regardless of what a therapist might have told me, as I felt internally driven to do it at the time. But I think I know what I *should* have done differently in hindsight. It's amazing how perspectives and priorities can become (and continue to be) distorted. Life's too short regardless of circumstances. Hopefully I can make some changes now.

This talk with Jeff led to some real soul searching and made me really think about what I want the rest of my life to be like. Yes, I'll still put Mary on the top of the list and I'll still visit her every day that I can, but hopefully my pursuit of her happiness will not be at the exclusion of everything and everyone else, and I can also put the rest of my life in better perspective. I need to strive for deeper relationships in the future…starting *now*.

A stark realization from my awakening was realizing that when Jeff, Ashley and their daughter joined Mary and me for dinner at our house, I often put Mary first over our granddaughter. More often than not, I sat on the couch with my arm around Mary, not on the floor playing. I think I was (sub) consciously trying to let *us* enjoy our granddaughter *together*. The same applies when our grandson and Mary were together. I realize now that my playing on the floor would have made little difference to Mary, but a lot of difference to our grandchildren, both short-term and long-term. Realizing this hit hard. It seems in this instance I had forgotten to "dance."

I hope nothing I've written seems to make light of Mary's condition or Alzheimer's in general. It's a horrible disease that leads to intensely sad times and difficult situations. My heart goes out to anyone affected by this or any other devastating illness. But under such circumstances, one can either be miserable and make everyone else miserable, or one can make the best of life and choose to be as happy as possible.

A quote by Jim Rohn seems appropriate:

"Happiness is not something you postpone for the future;
it is something you design for the present."

In many ways, throughout her journey with Alzheimer's and before, Mary used the present to the maximum for developing and designing her future.

Hopefully at least some of our experiences and ideas for what helped Mary and me that I've shared will help others with similar misfortunes. Or better yet, maybe it will provide some insight on preparing for the future, whether or not an illness such as Alzheimer's may lie ahead.

I mentioned at the beginning of this book that I wish I knew then what I know now. This ordeal has affected me immensely over the years, and I know I've changed in several ways. It's certainly given me great empathy for people who journey through these tribulations and great admiration for those who help them. These people and their families go through heart-wrenching challenges that no one should have to endure, yet often they make it through with heart-warming stories. A lot of my fears about the unknown have diminished because my mindset has changed.

I've learned from Mary that preparation and not giving up are the means to help overcome even the most difficult circumstances and experience love and happiness no matter what. Also key is accepting the situation—not being defeatist, but making the best of it, continuing to live life to the fullest.

While the diagnosis of Alzheimer's disease was devastating, Mary filled her heart, mind and spirit with good and Godly thoughts in her "preparation years," which prevailed later when the ability to rationally think about what she was going to say or do diminished. Both before and after the diagnosis, she didn't let Alzheimer's control her life or devastate our lives together. She felt good about herself, and her life was happier and healthier because of her efforts.

These accomplishments helped her enormously during her pre-diagnosis years and well into her post-diagnosis years, as they allowed her to achieve the result she desired. We can all learn from how Mary prepared for and handled herself after the diagnosis of Alzheimer's, whether we ever have a debilitating illness or not. I know I did.

Alzheimer's and the experiences that have come with it have changed my perspective on life, providing me with a new appreciation for how to deal with people who have problems, especially dementia, and how they can still be happy. After ordeals like this, those affected, both directly and indirectly, can have a new normal or setpoint—a different outlook on life for what's important.

I feel I've changed internally to a large extent with respect to my attitude, understanding and empathy, not only for Alzheimer's patients but others who are ill or "not normal." I've closely interacted with a lot of these people and realize they have continuing emotional needs and desires as we all do. I hope I've been able to alleviate some of the stigma of Alzheimer's and uncertainties of visiting and interacting with these special people.

It was difficult to write this book. I had taken notes from the beginning of Mary's experiences, especially during the most difficult periods, to help me know what to do, and to help professionals know how to best treat her. Recalling the bad times was painful and brought back lots of sad memories and stressful phases—times Mary and I were sometimes at odds with each other, which was so unlike our marriage before the disease took hold.

On the positive side, recalling these events had the effect of allowing me to be "pleased" with Mary's status now, at least compared to how unhappy and scared she had been at certain stages.

Now she has the advantage over me in that she doesn't remember the bad times—regretfully, she also doesn't remember the good times. Now, only the present counts for her, and every day can be good, as pleasant feelings are nurtured from one day to the next. One of my goals continues to be trying to make each day the best one ever for her.

The Serenity Prayer helped Mary through many years, and it helps me now. It tells me not to let what I cannot change or fix keep me from changing or fixing what I can. If I focus on the negatives, I can't make the most of the positives.

The title *Don't Forget to Dance* appealed to me because Mary always loved to dance. I didn't, but I wish I had danced with her more during our earlier years together. In some respects, I was allowed a "do-over," and since she's been in assisted living and memory care, I've danced with her in some way or another almost every day—in her room, in the elevator, at parties, walking down the hall. It makes her happy and she smiles. All of our feelings and interactions seem to be tied together with a rhythmical flow of emotions, which, over time, has turned into more of a combination of dance, communication, and sharing our love.

More importantly, *Don't Forget to Dance* has two important applications relevant to everyone. *Before* something limiting or "bad" happens, along with the fun stuff, do the things that fulfill your life, that give it purpose, that prepare you for a better future. Make the most of everything you love—the "dancing" in your life—developing strong relationships and creating great memories that will last as long as possible.

After a major health blow, like receiving an Alzheimer's diagnosis, it's important to still live life to the fullest, continuing doing what you enjoy and undertaking new adventures for as long as possible. This is not a time to give up.

For Mary, and hopefully any person with Alzheimer's, enjoying each moment engrains a few memories, or at least thoughts or feelings, in one's soul—enough to recall to bring about happiness. As many memories start to fade, Alzheimer's patients can experience peaceful, sometimes joyful, contented feelings that allow them to have good and even great days.

As Mary was in her preparation years, both before and after her diagnosis, she demonstrated how to seize the day—to make the most of what you have while you have it—and make your todays count so that your yesterdays and tomorrows also count. Mary prepared for her future, and her preparation paid off.

All of us are thrown obstacles in life, and we need to deal with these and move on as best as possible. Jimmy Dean said:

"I can't change the direction of the wind,
but I can adjust my sails to always reach my destination."

By adjusting my attitude and expectations, I feel I've been able to make the most of the present for both Mary and me, while also having a future destination to embrace.

I still smile in a warm, bittersweet moment hearing the cooing of mourning doves or seeing flickering fireflies, awe-inspiring sunsets, a full moon, horses galloping in a field, and many other scenes Mary loved so much. Such times make me miss her all the more. They also remind me of how she enjoyed the simple things in life and make me want to savor such moments.

I'm grateful Mary has been a part of my life. I know she has made my life better. She has touched the lives of many other people who have needed her help, and she has given them her time. Henry David Thoreau said:

"The price of anything is the amount of life you exchange for it."

For Mary it has been worth the price of her time and effort to help people and make their lives better. It's said one can look at a person's calendar to see what they valued in life. How Mary spent her time tells a lot. We all need to do what we can to make a significant difference in the world, in the lives of other people, or sometimes just in ourselves.

I feel blessed to have had my wife in a relatively healthy and happy state for as long as she has been. Since the situation couldn't be reversed, I wouldn't trade this time together for anything. Once the time comes, I will greatly miss her and our life together. No one knows how far off that will be or what experiences to expect from the next stages of her disease, but we have discussed various scenarios, and I know she wouldn't want to be in an unhappy or unknowing state for any lengthy time.

It will be hard to let go but I'm comforted in the knowledge that Mary had a good life overall, and I know I made it a better one for her. I feel good about that. I want to try to make Mary as happy as possible for the time remaining. I also have the comfort of knowing she's spiritually prepared for what comes next.

I strongly urge everyone to enjoy the good times and make the most of them while you can. It's easy to take something, or someone, for granted until you can no longer have them. Make a difference while you can so you don't later regret what could have been.

Do things together with loved ones, develop good friends, make nice memories, and *don't forget to dance.*

About the Author

Marc Alderdice has a PhD in pharmacology and has worked in academia, the pharmaceutical industry, and with contract research organizations specializing in the development of drugs used for neurological and psychiatric disorders. He has managed numerous clinical trials for experimental treatments of various medical disorders, some to test potential treatments for Alzheimer's disease.

Marc has also had the misfortune of dealing with Alzheimer's on a personal level when his wife, Mary, was diagnosed with early-onset Alzheimer's at the age of fifty-nine. He learned the hard way that living with Alzheimer's personally is much different and much more difficult than studying it objectively. His logical scientific approaches had to be abandoned in dealing with the struggles of Mary's, and thus his, life with Alzheimer's.

While his knowledge of Alzheimer's was helpful in some respects, *Don't Forget to Dance* is a personal and emotional memoir without scientific information to distract readers from the story—which is a true love story, not a science experiment. Marc's research background has helped his ongoing efforts to improve on Mary's happiness because he has not been hesitant to "experiment" with new methods to provide synergistic improvements for her happiness.

Made in United States
Orlando, FL
10 January 2022